RIDING
FOR THE
DISABLED

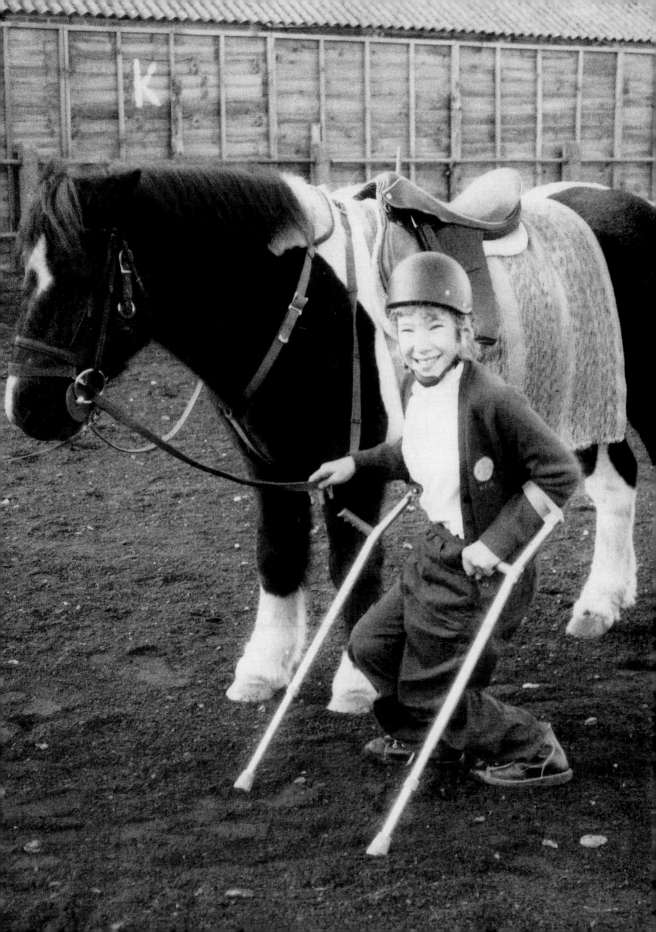

RIDING
FOR THE
DISABLED

Vanessa Britton

B. T. Batsford Ltd, London

This book is dedicated to everyone
involved, in whatever way, large or
small, with the Riding for the Disabled
movement worldwide; especially the
riders themselves who are so full of fun.

© Vanessa Britton 1991
First published 1991

ISBN 0 7134 6627 8

A CIP catalogue record for this book is available
from the British Library

Typeset by Keyspools Ltd, Golborne,
Lancashire and printed in Great Britain by
Butler & Tanner Ltd
Frome, Somerset
for the publishers
B. T. Batsford Ltd
4 Fitzhardinge Street
London W1H 0AH

*Frontispiece: Riding is a fun activity which
improves the general health of a rider with a
disability – the smile says it all.*

CONTENTS

LIST OF ILLUSTRATIONS

ACKNOWLEDGEMENTS

My very grateful thanks go to Jean Tebay who provided all of the American commentary including photographs and illustrations, without which the book would not have been possible. To Dick Moss for putting my name forward to write the book; for following it through and giving permission to use much RDA material. To the staff at RDA Headquarters for answering many queries. To Sister Chiara, Dr Gillian Peacock MB, ChB, MRCS, LRCP, and Yvonne Nelson BHSI, for offering helpful advice on the manuscript. To Geraldine Walker MCSP, for her help and advice on physiotherapy and Frances Thomas-Davies for information and diagrams on hippotherapy. To Lida McCowan for providing 'Aspects and Answers', and 'It is Ability That Counts.' To Elizabeth Beckerlegge and Anne Swinscow who took photographs especially for the book, and to the many people who also sent photographs for consideration. Photographs are taken by the author, except where the source is stated. To Gloria Dean who reproduced the special equipment diagrams from the RDA Handbook, and to everyone who offered information, advice and photographs.

My personal thanks go to all the people involved with the Member Groups of the RDA which I visited; especially to Moya Luddington and the team at the Magpie RDA Group. Also to the riders at this group who in many of the photographs are the 'stars of the show'. They put up with the disruption caused by my photo sessions and with my prying questions, showing me nothing but kindness. I am truly grateful.

INTRODUCTION

A history of riding for the disabled

People with disabilities have ridden horses since the days of the Ancient Greeks. There was no one set time in history when it was decided that people with disabilities could or should ride. The change that took place was in people's attitude toward riding for disabled individuals.

Not only were horses thought of as a means of transport at all times in history, but also as a way of helping to alleviate suffering and relieve handicaps. It was acknowledged that by the use of a horse the general health of the patient could be improved (2).

Riding was recognized as a beneficial form of therapy at the turn of the century by Dame Agnes Hunt, founder of the first Orthopaedic Hospital in Oswestry in 1901, and by Miss Olive Sands MCSP (Member of the Chartered Society of Physiotherapy); who during World War I took her horses to the Oxford Hospital, in the hope that men wounded in France, fearing rejection for further Army service, would benefit from riding experience. Through the commitment of these founder members, a seed was planted that has since germinated and grown. They could only hope that their belief that this form of therapy would help to broaden many handicapped people's horizons would be generally accepted in years to come. Not only has it now

been accepted, but also it is encouraged by many extremely dedicated people. Their beliefs have now been proven as fact many times over.

Many physiotherapists became active in this field in the 1950s. They were exploring the possibilities of riding for all types of handicaps, but in particular the victims of the polio epidemics of that time. Inspiration was provided through an excellent example set by Madame Liz Hartel. Not only did she overcome her handicap of polio, which partially paralysed her in both legs, but she also insisted on riding again. She progressed by sheer determination and extraordinary willpower, culminating in winning a silver medal in Dressage at the 1952 Helsinki Olympic Games, when women were competing with men on equal terms for the first time. For Madame Hartel the terms were not equal, yet she showed the world what she was capable of achieving with her much-loved horse, Jubilee.

The pyschological effects of Madame Hartel's success must have been tremendous: a train of thought picked up by Mrs Elsbeth Bödthker, a Norwegian physiotherapist and horsewoman of some standing herself. Early on in the 1950s, she and Miss Ulla Harpoth, another physiotherapist in Copenhagen, together with Liz Hartel, began to utilize riding as a form of therapy, encouraging their own patients to ride.

It was soon recognized that these patients were deriving numerous. benefits from this activity. Mrs Norah Jacques who actually knew Mrs

Bödthker, decided to try and establish something similar in Great Britain. She started in her back garden and later founded the **Pony Riding for the Disabled Trust**. Its director and head instructor at that time, John Anthony Davies, is now considered one of the world's leading authorities in this field. Miss Stella Saywell, who is also an authority on this subject, was the superintendent physiotherapist at Winford Orthopaedic Hospital, Bristol, which was the first hospital in Great Britain to use horseback riding as an officially prescribed therapy – as long ago as 1948. Another early pioneer, Dr Gillian Peacock MB, ChB, MRCS, LRCP is still heavily involved with riding for the disabled today. She is closely connected with the work of the **Riding for the Disabled Association** (RDA) and is responsible for liaising between medical bodies and those practising riding therapy in her capacity as Chairman of the Advisory Council of the **Fortune Centre of Riding Therapy**.

Suffice it to say that this form of therapy went from strength to strength; involving many truly dedicated people in Great Britain and other countries along the way.

'In general, the success of these ventures led to the formation of national organizations, which, in Europe, were recognized by financial support from governments. In Great Britain the British Horse Society (BHS) and Pony Club readily responded to requests for help.' (S. Y. Saywell)

In 1964 early UK pioneers came together to form the Advisory Council on Riding for the Disabled, which in 1969 went on to become the

2 *A child with central hypotonia receives sensory input from the rhythmic movement of the horse, enabling her to adapt to constant postural challenges thereby improving balance. (Anneke Davis. Photograph courtesy of the Center for Equine Therapy of Baltimore, Maryland.)*

Riding for the Disabled Association, as it is known today, with the added honour of having HRH The Princess Royal, GCVO, as the Association's President and Lavinia, Duchess of Norfolk, CBE, as Patron.

The RDA operates within the constraints of a National Registered Charity under a single banner (unlike the United States of America); its development has been dictated by this, and many overseas groups, including those in Australia, Canada and New Zealand, have benefited from its experience and, as a consequence, organized themselves in a similar way.

The Association could not operate as it does without the enormous enthusiasm and dedication of voluntary helpers, and in that situation there is a limit to the degree of standardization and bureaucratic requirements that can be imposed from the centre. The Association works on the basis of goodwill and a genuine desire to serve people with disabilities through the medium of riding.[1]

The RDA teaches riding on a voluntary basis for the purpose of giving enjoyment and improving the quality of life of the riders. RDA riders attend RDA riding lessons to learn to ride, not for therapeutic benefit, although the spin-offs of such riding are therapeutic.

A history of riding for the disabled in the United States[2]

Riding for the disabled in the United States has developed differently; not solely to teach individuals with disabilities to ride but in the main being conducted for its therapeutic benefits, and therefore needs its own explanation.

Established programmes of riding for the handicapped in the United States date back to the 1960s, when several independent activities were being conducted by dedicated horsepeople and clinicians who volunteered both their animals and their time. From this modest beginning came great growth and diversification.

The most widely recognized of the American therapeutic riding associations is the North American Riding for the Handicapped Association (NARHA), with a recreational, educational and therapeutic emphasis. The founding of NARHA in 1969, by Alexander MacKay Smith of Middleburg, Virginia, then editor of *The Chronicle of the Horse*, Lida L. McCowan, director of the Cheff Center in Augusta, Michigan, and John A. Davies of the Chigwell Centre in Great Britain, enabled groups across the country to have a central advisory body to coordinate the efforts of the movement, establish safety guidelines and disseminate information to both individual and group members. NARHA's ongoing mission is to train and certify competent instructors, to accredit centres which meet its standards for safety and operation, and to promote research to investigate scientifically the use of the horse as a therapeutic tool. Additionally, NARHA offers its operating centres, which numbered 461 in 1989, the opportunity to participate in a comprehensive insurance scheme, including liability coverage for centres as well as their directors and officers. Such an insurance scheme is of great importance given the potential in the United States for litigation.

No history of the development of riding for the handicapped in the United States would be complete without the mention of Happy Horsemanship for the Handicapped (HHFTH), founded by Maudie Hunter-Warfel in 1967. Its major aim is the enjoyment of the horse by handicapped people. The approach is holistic and includes the total environment surrounding the horse. Therapy is the result, not the aim. Several persons affiliated with this organization have received national recognition in the United States for their efforts. Of special note is Dave Trexler of Al Marah Farm in Tucson, Arizona, Arab breeding farm manager, horse trainer and competitive western rider, who is a double amputee.

NASCP, the United States National Association of Sports for Cerebral Palsy was founded in

3 *Jim, a rider with mental handicaps, participating in a Special Olympics horsemanship event, held in Wisconsin in October 1989. Note the use of English reins, and Western saddle. (Special Olympics International)*

1976 as a branch of the United Cerebral Palsy Association, Inc., to provide competitive sport opportunities for individuals with cerebral palsy and related conditions. Following the Olympic model, a wide range of sports, including equestrian events, are incorporated for athletes who are grouped according to their degree of functional involvement. An increasing number of individuals with physical disabilities are seeking the challenges inherent in dressage, equitation and handy rider competitive events offered at the NASCP games.

Special Olympics, Inc., differing from the NASCP, which provides competition for those who are of average intelligence, is the sports governing body for individuals with some form of mental handicap. Currently, approximately 4000 athletes are in training, representing 36 states. Trained coaches number 750. Additionally, an estimated twelve countries are involved at the international level. Riders compete in an impressive array of activities, including dressage, Prix Caprilli, equitation, working trails, barrel racing, pole bending and team relays. Showmanship, both in-hand and ridden, is also offered, with the emphasis more on the athlete's ability to present his or her horse than on the breed and conformation of the animal being shown. Rules have yet to be developed for drill teams of two and four, though some competition in this exists. A complete competition training manual has been developed, as well as a summer rule book. A venue guide is being prepared for publication in 1990 (3). Two key individuals deserve recognition for their contribution to this work: Octavia J. Brown, long-time NARHA board member of Bedminster, New Jersey, and Mary-Lu Bonte of Laurel, Maryland, current director of Equestrian Sports for Special Olympics.[3]

The Delta Society, established in 1976, is an international education, research and service resource on the relationship between people, animals and the environment. Although the relationship between horse and man is only one component of its broad concern, riding as therapy receives focused attention at its conferences and in its publications. At the outset, the Delta Society provided a forum where representatives of therapeutic riding groups with philosophical and practical differences could explore areas of common interest and concern. More recently, the society has offered two annual awards in therapeutic riding, one for model programme and one for outstanding therapy horse. In addition, each year the society presents the Michael J. McCulloch Memorial Award, which honours a human health professional for outstanding research, teaching or service that increases our understanding of the interaction between people and companion or therapy animals. In 1989 this award was presented to Mary Woolverton, of Littleton, Colorado, for her pioneering work with disabled Vietnam veterans and horses.[4]

Yet another United States national organization which is involved in therapeutic riding is the 4-H youth clubs of America. 4-H originated in the early 1900s as a way to involve farm youths in related agricultural and social activities. Its involvement in riding for the handicapped began in the 1970s, with the State of Michigan leading the way with a comprehensive programme initiated by Michigan State University's Cooperative Extension Service. At the present time, Pennsylvania's 4-H clubs are also heavily involved. Their organization, the Pennsylvania Council of Horseback Riding for the Handicapped, disseminates an informational quarterly newsletter and sponsors educational seminars and instructor training courses for all statewide therapeutic riding personnel.[5]

RIDERS IN THEIR OWN RIGHT

Riding is a pleasurable activity for many people. It is a social skill that can be great fun for all involved. It is also an escape for many children and adults with disabilities, who might otherwise be confined to a wheelchair. For many, it provides mobility, which allows them to get from a to b, but it is also much more than that. There is a different aspect to riding, one which most able-bodied riders would never think of, and that is its therapeutic benefits, and how it helps disabled individuals in their general health.

How does riding help people with disabilities?

How much a person with a disability can benefit from riding will depend firstly on the disability they have, mental or physical; and secondly on the form of riding therapy offered.

Therapeutic riding encompasses many different activities; from **sports riding** for people with disabilities, to **remedial educational riding**, to the medical application of the horse as **hippotherapy**. There is also vaulting and driving for the disabled. Each of these activities enjoys certain shared benefits, while each has benefits unique to the specific activity.

Shared benefits

Almost every disabled individual involved in therapeutic riding experiences the benefits we often read about: **improved general health and well-being**, cardiovascular system gains, stimulation of the basic body functions, including bowel and bladder function and those of other inner organs, and a positive influence on the support and movement structure of the body. In addition, there are often improvements in head and trunk control, equilibrium reactions and body awareness.

Many handicapped individuals find that participation in most sports and recreational activities is difficult. However, riding is a sport in which people with disabilities can participate successfully, and often with only minor modifications or adaptations.

Physically handicapped riders are quite capable of understanding how to ride a horse, but may be prevented from doing so by their handicap. In this case they may either learn new techniques or use special equipment. Mentally handicapped people may be quite capable physically of riding a horse, but without help may be prevented from doing so by their lack of understanding and communication. Once they are provided with this help, in the form of the instructors, teachers, physiotherapists, trained helpers and horses that make up the therapeutic riding team, they may develop their communic-

4 The instructor, teacher, physiotherapist, trained helpers, riders and ponies make up the therapeutic riding team.

ation skills and their ability to understand (**4**). Many handicapped riders may have both mental and physical disabilities.

People with disabilities happily go riding. When they are astride a horse they are not necessarily thinking of the benefits they are deriving. Their first thoughts are the same as any other rider, and that is – what good fun it is. To be looking down on somebody for the first time in their lives is a very uplifting experience.

Riding is a stimulating challenge which gives **greater confidence and independence** to the riders, in turn making them very happy. Often it provides a very important interest, which may be the only independent activity taken outside the rider's normal environment. There is also a great **sense of achievement** when something new has been accomplished.

Another benefit is the encouragement of fitness. Riding a horse keeps the disabled individual active, exercising many parts of the body at once. Done on a regular basis, riding stimulates the rider to **increased fitness** and maintains that fitness.

Bonding

Bonding is another important benefit for those handicapped individuals who ride. Often, the individual with a disability has difficulty building friendships. But in an equestrian setting the horse becomes the focus of attention. The disabled rider develops a friendship with his horse, often talking to the horse about his innermost thoughts and feelings. An important aspect of this relationship is due to the fact that horses are non-verbal. This allows the rider the freedom to express himself fully without fear of rejection or criticism. The horse becomes a willing listener; quiet, attentive and approving (5).

It has been proven that the horse acts as a motivator or stimulator for certain individuals with disabilities. For example, the individual who has become tired of physical therapy in a classic clinical environment will come to the riding setting for his treatment, arriving on time, eagerly anticipating the treatment session and participating actively in the therapy regimen. He will try hard to accomplish the tasks set for him by the physiotherapist. In this way he experiences a sense of accomplishment, as well as improvement in his physical condition. These feelings in turn encourage him to continue and to return again for the next treatment.

Socialization is another of the shared benefits of riding. Many individuals with disabilities spend long hours of each day isolated from the real world. They are often educated in special schools; or, in those circumstances where they are integrated into regular classrooms, they are treated with a certain deference which also serves as a type of isolation. In riding, however, normal social interaction takes place on many different levels; especially with peers who come for the riding lesson. Here, all riders swap stories and experiences energetically and enthusiastically, participating together as a group in this enjoyable activity.

On another level, because of the number of helpers often required for a handicapped rider to participate in riding, the rider must develop a relationship with his helpers in order to communicate more successfully with the horse. On a third level, once the rider leaves the riding setting, he goes back into his world eager to report to those around him about his riding experiences, his triumphs and successes.

5 *Let's make friends.*

Specific benefits

For individuals with specific sensory deficits, the horse can be a rewarding partner, offering compensation for the rider. As an example, let us take the deaf rider who may be unable to hear an approaching truck on the road, or a barking dog. The horse, however, does hear, and alerts his rider by a variety of body signals, including raising his head and neck, tensing his muscles and turning his ears towards the sound. The deaf rider must, of course, be taught to interpret the language of the horse, but once this is accomplished the rider can then depend on the animal to provide important sensory information.

Vaulting is simply defined as gymnastics on horseback. But when adapted for riding for the disabled, it moves beyond the performance of certain set manoeuvres and becomes a remedial education tool for learning disabled and emotionally disturbed children. This type of vaulting has been thoroughly documented by Antonius Kroger of Germany. In his many treatises on the subject he has described the following benefits: diminished anxieties, diminished hyperactivity, increased levels of trust, increased ability for correct self-evaluation, increased self-esteem, improvement in sensory-motor skills, gains in interpersonal skills, diminished aggressive tendencies, diminished dislikes and phobias and an overall increase in the development of positive social behaviour patterns.

The medical benefits are also noteworthy, with co-ordination and balance being improved. Riding is a treatment which helps to overcome disability and to reduce handicap. The most important factor to recognize when deciding upon a disabled person's form of therapy is whether that person has an acute illness or a chronic disability, as Professor K. S. Holt, who is professor of developmental paediatrics at The Wolfson Centre, Institute of Health, explains in a paper by Dr Lee Burton on *The Value of Riding Therapy For The Mentally Handicapped Child*:

The very considerable difference between acute illnesses on the one hand and chronic disabilities on the other hand are seldom recognized, and many doctors even regard them all as medical disorders.

An acute illness is a self-limiting event. After a period of time the individual recovers as a result of either spontaneous natural remission or successful treatment. Once the acute episode is over, the individual returns to his former pattern of life and development.

Chronic disabilities persist. There is no opportunity for the individual to return to a previous pattern of life and development; he has to live his life and strive to develop as best he can despite his disabilities, and the extent to which he falls short is a measure of his handicap. Consequently, any chronically disabled individual needs to be helped by receiving appropriate treatment for the disability and also assistance to reduce his handicap. Treatments which achieve both aims, i.e. overcome disability and reduce handicap, are especially useful. Riding for the mentally handicapped is in this category.

In the medical applications of the horse as a means of treatment, there is yet another set of specific benefits. The rider, now called a patient, is affected by the movements of the horse. These movements act on the mounted patient's body to improve the patient's **posture**, **balance**, **mobility** and **function** (2).

During a hippotherapy session, the trained physiotherapist analyses the patient's responses to the moving horse. The physiotherapist then adjusts the horse's movements according to the needs of the patient to elicit certain positive patient responses. The warmth of a horse combined with its gentle movement helps to reduce spasticity, encourages the development of the lumbar curve, missing in many floppy or mentally handicapped riders, and encourages head and neck control.

Riding for handicapped individuals encompasses all activities relating to the horse; therefore, not only does a rider benefit from the actual activity of riding but also from related activities such as stable management. Often, riders with a mental or physical handicap can relate to the things they experience more easily than to things they are told. When they are riding a horse, they get an instant feedback. If they pull the right rein, the horse turns to the right. If they pull both reins, he stops. If they do not do these things nothing happens. This is how the learning process evolves. One action provides one response. In this way a rider not only benefits by learning to ride, but also in physical and mental wellbeing. Communication with a horse, which responds to actions, is often easier than communication with another person, who responds to words.

Horses themselves are therapists. They provide the most important quality of the riding experience and that is the ability to unknowingly motivate their riders. With the help of the instructor, physiotherapist and helpers who form the therapeutic riding team this stimulus can be maximized. It is often very difficult in certain cases to know when and when not to help. It is a mistake to help a rider with a disability if they can manage without. The emphasis must be on the rider's ability, not disability.

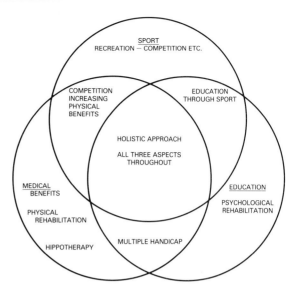

6 *A three-circle diagram illustrating the different areas within the field of therapeutic riding (Dr Gillian Peacock MB, ChB, MRCS, LRCP)*

In the 1970s, the Germans, who were developing a theoretical construct for therapeutic riding, designed a three-circle illustration to describe the differences within the field.[1] These three main sections (**6**) are internationally recognized. This three-circle diagram applies to riding for individuals with disabilities worldwide. However, in the United Kingdom the concepts of sport, medicine and education might be explained as the physical, mental and emotional impact riding provides as a therapeutic medium.

Riding therapy

The different aspects of riding therapy differ from country to country. Internationally, some countries place a greater emphasis on one aspect rather than another, mostly depending on the funding for the activity. However, the three main sections are:

1 **Pure therapy**
2 **Combined leisure and therapy** (which can be subdivided)
3 **Pure leisure**

Physical therapy (medicine)

This is using riding as a form of treatment and the horse and its movement to gain a specific effect on the rider with disabilities.

The term **hippotherapy** was coined by a group of physicians and therapists in Germany in the 1960s and is widely used in Europe by therapists to describe a medical treatment method using the horse as a therapeutic intervention. In Germany it is sometimes used as a treatment for people who suffer from minor problems such as backache. They will have treatment on the lunge, but are usually quite capable of riding. However, it is mainly used as a treatment method for individuals with disabilities, where some patients may never be capable of riding independently. Indeed, the aim of hippotherapy is not to teach riding skills, but to concentrate on the therapeutic benefits. The horse influences the patient, rather than the patient controlling the horse. During treatment the physiotherapist positions the patient on the horse, analyses the patient's response to the horse and directs the movements of the horse. Because of this, it can only be performed by a physiotherapist who is skilled in this field and who also has knowledge of riding. It should be done as an

7 Hippotherapist Barbara L. Glasow, PT, is able to focus safely on improving the posture and balance of a young cerebral palsy quadriplegic on a horse through the use of backriding. (Barbara L. Glasow, PT)

individual treatment and not within a group lesson. When and if a rider progresses to more independent status, he may then be able to ride within a group. The goal of hippotherapy, however, is to improve the patient's **posture**, **balance**, **mobility** and **function**.

Back riding is normally part of hippotherapy and the role of the physiotherapist is to give a treatment using the horse while seated on the horse behind the rider (7). The movement of the horse at the walk transmits a three-dimensional movement to the rider which stimulates a normal walking pattern and can give a rider who is unable to walk the sensation of an easy gait.

This medical application of the horse uses a team approach involving the physician/doctor, the physiotherapist and the riding specialist, especially in the United States. This is also beginning to be practised in Great Britain.

Other medical uses of the horse include developmental hippotherapy, developmental riding therapy and developmental vaulting. Each uses a team approach and each has medical remediation as the major objective.

Developmental Riding Therapy,[2] as developed by New Harmony Foundation, is a treatment system which specifically addresses the individual rider's cognitive, affective, perceptual motor, and/or movement competency needs. This system is considered a psychomotor discipline which is uniquely American. Professionals with graduate-level degrees in rehabilitation/ psychomotricity, psychology, special education, speech pathology, adapted physical education, or occupational therapy, utilize this speciality approach for conditions such as autism, learning/language delay, sensory integration disorder, emotional disturbance, mental retardation, mild cerebral palsy or post-traumatic brain injury. Placing two children in opposing side-sit positions, as an example of developmental riding therapy, illustrates the following: a) the role of the psychomotor team, b) the utilization of prescriptive movement input from the horse in combination with developmental positions, and

c) identifiable objective areas such as body image/mirroring, laterality and dynamic postural adjustment via graded equilibrium disturbance and appropriate focused attention (8).

8 An example of Developmental Riding Therapy. (Jan Spink, MA, New Harmony Foundation)

9 Riders are performing exercises, selected by the physiotherapist to improve balance and coordination.

Combined leisure and therapy (education)

Combined leisure and therapy (education) can be sub-divided into remedial group therapy and leisure in the form of hacks, games and the like. Equine activities, including riding, driving and vaulting, are used to gain educational, remedial and psychotherapeutic benefits for individuals with physical, mental and psychological impairments. The emphasis is on incorporating cognitive, behavioural, psycho-social and physical goals into the activity while teaching adapted skills. The horse acts as a motivator for accomplishing these goals. Here the therapeutic effect is being achieved by riders without them being aware of it.

Remedial group riding helps teach riders with disabilities how to ride and how to improve their physical and mental abilities by progressive achievable goals. **Remedial games** and other leisure activities can be selected to achieve particular goals for each rider (9).

Riding out on hacks or at picnics give changes in surface, up- and downhill rides, rough ground and wider views, all of which help to stimulate the mind and provide freedom of movement and a sense of achievement. Games help achieve the riders' individual goals if they are allowed to perform to their maximum and do not have the game played for them with the aim of winning. The riders will gain far more if they do a task on their own and come in last, rather than win by someone else doing it. **Driving** is an excellent alternative for the severely disabled. Combined leisure and therapy also applies to driving for the disabled.

In Great Britain there are purpose-built

centres which practise this form of riding therapy, and many RDA member group sessions also work in this way.

Pure leisure (sport)

This aspect includes sports such as dressage, hacking, show jumping, gymkhana games, handy pony and riding holidays. These can be graded from those done just for disabled riders, to full integration with able-bodied riders.

Within the broad spectrum of **sport**, equine activities are adapted so that individuals with physical, mental and psychological impairments can participate. The activities include **riding**, **driving** and **vaulting** as forms of recreation and competition. Psychological and educational benefits are often achieved by those involved in these adaptive sports programmes (**10**). However, the primary objective is to teach the skills involved in the sport, which has been adapted to suit the individual needs of the participant.

The physiotherapist's role in this field is mostly to advise riders how to be able to achieve more, either by doing specific exercises to improve something, or how to adapt to a disability and make the most of it. A watch is kept on all riders to see that they are riding with the least possible risk to themselves and are not becoming overtired or stressed. Pure leisure therapy also applies to driving for the disabled.

The range of interaction between horse and disabled rider extends from enjoyment of the horse as an end in itself, through riding for sport and recreation, to the thrill of competition; riding for behaviour change, for educational benefits; and the use of the movement of the horse for therapy. Worldwide, there is an effort to respond to the needs of each rider in a creative and

10 *A rider participating in a handy pony competition, where one of the tasks is to keep the pony still in a square of straw bales for one minute. (Moya Luddington)*

personal way. The riding session is regarded as a holistic experience with implications for the whole person. Co-operation and communication among the many groups within and outside Great Britain and the United States are leading to continued growth and development of this unique use of the horse.

Who can ride?

Riding and driving are provided for a wide variety of handicaps and disabilities, both mental and physical. There are some governing factors which may sometimes prevent certain people from riding. If it has been shown that a rider may damage himself beyond minor injuries should he suffer a fall (although this is unlikely owing to the amount of supervision he receives at all times), then his doctor will recommend that he does not ride. However, riding is regarded as a risk sport and as such the benefits for and against riding have been extensively looked at. **Safety** is a very important factor when considering whether a person with a handicap should ride. Doctors, qualified physiotherapists, occupational therapists and experienced riding instructors should be consulted before going ahead with any riding session.

It is not only the rider that has to be considered, but the mount also. Many riders, since they do not get much exercise, are quite heavy. In this case a larger horse must be used. This is not always ideal, as its height creates more problems for the helpers and it may even make its rider apprehensive. An alternative for the severely handicapped, or for a rider who is too heavy for normal mounts, is driving.

Disabilities

Everyone involved in riding for the disabled tries to be familiar with the different disabilities commonly encountered in riding groups. A background of each rider's case should be available to the instructor, and for the information of the team. However, this material is confidential, and must be kept so. Groups are sometimes split into sessions for physically and mentally handicapped riders, although combined disability is very common.

What role does the doctor play in riding for the disabled?

Without the doctor's approval, no person with a disability can ride or drive. **Medical consent** is essential in all cases because the doctor is ultimately the person responsible for the patient's health. Once a doctor has referred a person for riding, the responsibility is then shared by the group physiotherapist and the riding instructor.

The rider's doctor will take many things into consideration when deciding whether to refer a patient for riding. He is the one who knows exactly what is wrong with the patient and he will of course be aware of the patient's medical history. He may be able to advise the group physiotherapist and instructor of the best way of handling the rider, especially if the rider has any special needs. As well as knowing what disability a rider has, it is useful if the doctor can fill in some other medical details. He can inform the physiotherapist and instructor of any surgery the rider has undergone. He may be able to provide an assessment of the rider's psychological state and provide an estimate of the rider's IQ.

The group instructor must know whether the rider takes any medication, and any possible side effects. Certain defects must be known, such as those affecting speech, hearing, sight, the circulation, sensation, co-ordination and balance. Although some of these defects will be known to attend certain disabilities, they may not be obvious at first. Some riders suffer from incontinence and it is therefore necessary to know what appliance the rider uses and how to give any necessary assistance. It is obvious that the group instructor must know of these things. The rider's doctor will be aware if the rider suffers from any of these conditions and it is in his, his patient's and the group instructor's best interests if he makes all things known from the start.

The doctor will also be able to advise on any appliances and braces. However, he may be very busy and therefore may not have the chance to follow the rider's progress as closely as he might like. It would be beneficial for a doctor in this situation if both the group instructor and the group physiotherapist could report back any significant progress or findings.

The medical profession in general was at first slow to become involved in this area of therapy. Medical practitioners were sometimes reluctant to give their consent for their patients to be involved in a risk sport which might cause further disability to the patient. Once it was shown, through tests and experimental studies, that riders benefited from improved general health, physical skills, motivation and enjoyment, the medical profession then began to refer patients for riding therapy.

Most doctors referring patients for riding in Great Britain are those that work in special schools for the handicapped. Very few riders are referred by the general practitioner. In the case of an individual member of the public, it is often a parent or a physiotherapist who approaches the doctor with a view to a particular child or adult riding. The doctor may then evaluate the case and make his decision. It is hoped that a larger proportion of doctors may become more aware in future that riding is of great benefit to many riders with disabilities.

Where do riders with disabilities come from?

The majority of riders with disabilities come from special schools for the disabled, adult training centres or hospitals, although approximately five per cent of the total amount of riders in Great Britain are private riders. Selection is usually through physiotherapists or teachers or self-referrals. Riding is provided for both **adults** and **children**; however, more children than adults ride, with two-thirds of riders being under 18 in Great Britain. Sometimes riding opportunities for adults are limited. Few groups are able to arrange riding sessions in the evening, either due to lack of facilities or because helpers are unable to attend. Because of this a proportion of disabled adults in training centres or in private work have little chance of riding. They may be able to ride at weekends, but the same problems are encountered with helpers and/or facilities. Often riding schools will allow riding for disabled groups to use their facilities in off-peak times such as daytime during the week. They cannot, of course, allow the facilities to be used at weekends, when most of their own clients wish to ride. There are few purpose-built centres for disabled riders in Great Britain, so riding for this group of adults remains a problem.

Many special schools for people with disabilities integrate riding programmes within the normal school timetable. Schools of this nature are very beneficial to riders with disabilities and they often carry on with horse studies in the classroom. Disabled riders in this environment gain the maximum possible benefit.

While children are at school, riding is organized for them. Once away from school, the initiative is theirs, unless they are in an adult training centre which is able to arrange riding sessions to suit both the centre and riding school.

There is a distinction in Great Britain between the RDA, which teaches riding on a voluntary basis for the purpose of giving enjoyment and improving the quality of life of the riders, and the Fortune Centre of Riding Therapy, which operates a unique educational programme offering education and rehabilitation through horse motivation (see Chapter 8). The Fortune Centre is concerned with therapy, and does this very professionally. The end objective is to improve their pupils educationally. At the Fortune Centre alone well over £300,000 per annum of government funds in Great Britain are being put into two-year residential further education through horsemastership courses for less handicapped school leavers.

Sudden disablement

Sudden disablement is traumatic for anyone. People may suddenly become disabled for many reasons. They may have sustained injuries in an accident, which could have resulted in amputation, blindness, deafness, head traumas, or even strokes which may lead to paralysis. There are of course other sudden disablements, but the effects on the patient's initial outlook will be the same.

For people who have never ridden and who have become suddenly disabled, riding can provide help. They often feel that they are useless, or that they cannot cope with their disablement. Riding provides an environment where they are on equal terms with other people, not just other people with disabilities but able-bodied people as well. For somebody who has lost mobility, the horse provides four strong legs. For somebody who can no longer see, the horse sees for them, yet they are able to take an active part in where they are going.

Riders who have ridden before, yet become suddenly disabled, often feel that they will never sit on a horse again. Investigation has shown that many people who previously rode competently have given up, after losing a leg, for example. Once they have found the ability to cope with the disability, they often regret their decision not to carry on riding. There are ways and means for many disabled riders to carry on effective riding, providing active and stimulating exercise. Much re-learning and practice is involved, with determination on the rider's part being essential. Sometimes people do not continue to ride after they become disabled because they lack help and encouragement. The joys of able-bodied riding may seem lost to them for ever: thus the battle is lost before it is begun. With due consideration given to the problems and to their possible solutions, riding in a form that suits individual needs can once more become a part of their lives.

IT'S A PARTNERSHIP

In Great Britain, the whole spectrum of riding for the disabled can be split into three categories which can be closely related to each other, as described in Chapter 1. The instructors, physiotherapists, special teachers and trained helpers work as a team throughout the categories, with a few exceptions in hippotherapy, which is a one-to-one activity practised by some physiotherapists who are experts in their own field and are knowledgeable horsepeople as well. In the Uni-

ted States therapeutic riding has been organized into three primary fields representing the three different approaches – sport, remedial educational riding and vaulting, and the medical uses of the horse – and three different types of teams practise the three approaches.

11 *Treatment team in adapted sports riding (Developed by Jean Tebay from idea by Heipertz)*

TREATMENT TEAM
IN ADAPTED SPORTS RIDING

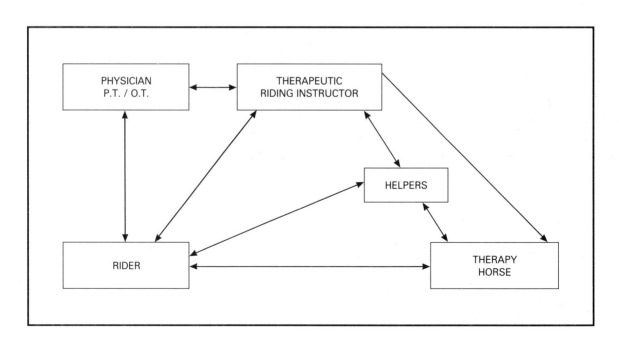

Whether the one-team approach, as preferred in Great Britain, or the specific team, as organized in the United States, is applied, the aim for riders with disabilities is to benefit their general health through riding.

Who are the team players?

In sport/pure-leisure riding, which includes riding, driving and vaulting, all as recreational activity or in competition, the riding instructor is the individual primarily responsible for the design and implementation of the RDA group. In this aspect of therapeutic riding, the adjunct professionals, who in this case might include the **doctor/physician** or other **medical professionals** or **education specialists**, can act as consultants to the **riding instructor**, giving advice about the special needs of the riders (**11**).

In psycho-remedial educational riding and vaulting/combined leisure and therapy, where there is a strong emphasis on psychological goals, the role of the riding instructor changes. Here a true team approach is employed, with the instructor acting as a member of a teaching team in which special education personnel, therapeutic recreation specialists and/or psychologists are actively involved as consultants in the day-to-day design and conduct of the riding session. In this setting, therapy is the primary focus. Riding, driving and vaulting skills are adapted for specific therapeutic benefits. The horse supplies the motive for achieving the goals in the rider's therapeutic programme (**12**).

12 *Treatment team in psycho-remedial-educational riding and vaulting*

TREATMENT TEAM
IN PSYCHO-REMEDIAL-EDUCATIONAL
RIDING AND VAULTING

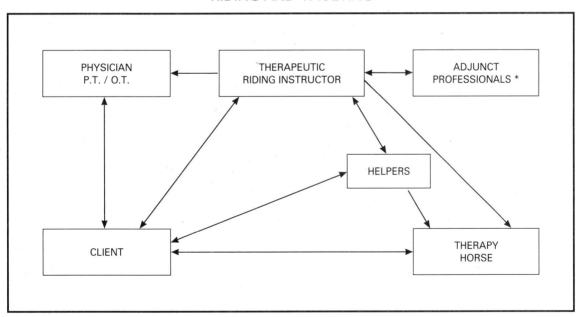

* Adjunct professionals include recreation therapists, special educators, and psychologists.

TREATMENT TEAM IN HIPPOTHERAPY

A hippotherapist is a physical or occupational therapist with additional training in the use of equine movement to treat patients with minimal to severe movement disorders.

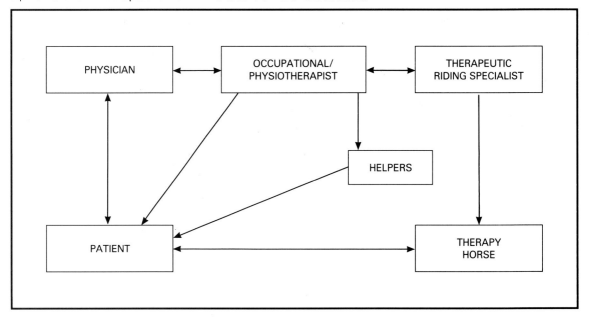

13 *Treatment team in hippotherapy (Heipertz)*

In the medical/pure therapy use of the horse, the team approach is used once again. Here, the physician/doctor is an important member of the team. When the direct services of a physical or occupational therapist are necessary, United States state law may require a physician's pre-scription for this service, in which case the physician must write a prescription for the disabled individual to seek hippotherapy as a specific treatment with set therapeutic goals. As in Great Britain, in every aspect of therapeutic riding the physician attending the rider/client/patient is asked to complete a physician's medical history form. A medical release form from the physician is essential for insurance reasons. The medical history form gives the riding programme personnel inform-ation about the rider that may affect the riding programme (**13**).

After review of the medical history the riding team will decide whether or not the individual is a candidate for riding. Factors which influence this decision include:

1 Does his or her condition present medical contra-indications?

The absolute contra-indications are:

a) Unhealed pressure sores

b) Fragile bones

c) Haemophilia

d) Uncontrolled (by drugs) epilepsy

e) Disinclination to ride – after experience

2 Does the riding group have the appropriate staff? (For example, a group without a physio-therapist would not take an individual with severe physical disabilities.)

3 Does the group have the appropriate horses? (For example, a group should not accept a large adult if a horse that can carry such weight is not available.)

It is the final responsibility of the staff to accept or deny any prospective rider. A quality group accepts only those individuals that it has the facility, equipment, animals and expertise to serve.

Who helps? Who cares?

The therapeutic riding instructor

The therapeutic riding instructor, out of all those involved in riding groups, is the nucleus of the whole operation. Yet, he or she knows full well that he is a member of a team, who are all striving together to achieve the same aims. He has to use his own initiative, but does not work alone. The instructor is the nucleus, but the team is the cell from which his ideas and personality must grow.

A riding instructor teaches people to ride. The instructor in a disabled riding group also teaches people to ride and although he may use different methods to achieve this goal, he will follow the BHS recommendations as closely as possible. He must at all times try to produce results, although this is not easy and may sometimes be hopeless. To help him in this aim, he must possess certain qualities. He must have the utmost patience with both adults and children. He must be sensitive to their needs, on or off a horse. He must have the ability to motivate his riders and influence them in their actions, maximizing the rider's potential.

Of course an instructor must be able to ride, but he need not be an expert in any competitive field. Being able to demonstrate certain requirements is all that is necessary. What he does need, however, is a **positive approach** to all that he does. He is the person who bears most of the responsibility for all activities of riders with disabilities. He must provide a happy atmosphere, even when he has his own problems. Foremost in his mind must be the element of safety – he must not let his mind wander on to other things. The ability to 'put a brave face on it' is a great ability indeed. A total commitment is needed, 99 per cent will not do. If a rider is to progress, he will look to the instructor for help and assurance. A **smile** can convey to a rider who has limited understanding a message that he has achieved the goal for that lesson.

The instructor must have a good understanding of all disabilities of all riders under his care. He must know how his actions will influence each rider, why such action will help a particular rider's equestrian skill, and why such actions will benefit the rider's overall well-being.

The instructor has many practical duties he must perform. First of all he must appear smart and tidy, somebody who is to be looked up to and respected. He must have a sense of humour, which must show in his whole attitude towards each lesson given. His attitude towards the whole riding programme must show him to be totally dedicated to the riding for the disabled movement and all those involved with it. The key qualities in the instructor are enthusiasm, caring, sensitivity, patience, equitation knowledge, communication skills, teaching ability and perhaps most of all the ability to motivate not only the riders, but also the physiotherapists and helpers as well.

In general, the job of conducting a successful riding lesson falls on the shoulders of the instructor. His or her jobs are many and varied and include the following:[1]

- Assign and supervise helpers in duties, jobs and responsibilities
- Know aspects of disabilities of population being served
- Conduct volunteer helper training
- Exercise and train therapeutic riding horses
- Perform stable management duties required for horses
- Perform rider evaluations
- Devise therapeutic lesson plans
- Supervise riding arena preparation
- Conduct therapeutic riding lessons
- Establish and maintain safety standards
- Conduct or supervise all mounting and

dismounting procedures

- Write therapeutic riding student progress reports
- Select horses, tack and special equipment for riders with disabilities
- Select horse appropriate for rider disability
- Develop a team approach and command the full co-operation of the team members

The person with perhaps the greatest burden of responsibility in this whole scheme is the instructor: he is the one in closest contact, on him everyone relies, and for him everyone concerned in the group contributes. This is not a burden to be borne lightly, and great sacrifices will be expected both mentally and physically. To the rider with disabilities the instructor is perhaps the one person who gives hope for a brighter future, so the teacher must never underestimate the task before him.[2]

The physiotherapist

The role of the physiotherapist in riding groups, is to work with the instructor and helpers to gain maximum benefit for each rider by using his or her full potential. This can be achieved by advising on suitable exercises, progressions, where to support or hold and what form of stimulus to provide. The physiotherapist should also teach and assist with correct mounting and dismounting techniques and rider handling in general.

Physiotherapists understand the physical problems encountered in everyday life and can help to combat them with the help of riding. They are trained to know how each muscle, joint and ligament works, and which exercise or form of activity will benefit each individual problem. They are more concerned with improving the rider's ability, so benefiting his health in general. They may not be experts in riding, but they will be able to see wrong posture and movement and advise how to correct it.

They will be able to advise the instructor on each rider's disability, giving helpful advice as to what physical activities each rider should undertake in order to help each disability and advise on the physical limits of individuals.

Together the instructor and physiotherapist can carry out an initial assessment of individual riders, determining the individual's ability to progress. They will be able to plan a programme of the right kind to help the rider develop his equestrian skills and his ability in other tasks.

As the physiotherapist advises in each case, the instructor will be acquiring knowledge of how to deal with recurring problems in the same or subsequent individuals. However, the instructor must never take the place of a physiotherapist or vice versa. Group physiotherapists should try to make themselves available to hold regular briefing sessions for helpers, explaining disabilities in general terms and individual problems.

The Association of Chartered Physiotherapists in Riding for the Disabled (ACPRD), a clinical interest section of the Chartered Society of Physiotherapy with approximately 200 members at present, provides a nucleus of physiotherapists working in or interested in this field. Not all RDA group physiotherapists are members but the society is working towards this end. Many groups tend to recruit a local physiotherapist, who may or may not have knowledge of horses or the effects of riding, but this is not ideal. Physiotherapists who come into this category should seek riding experience, so that they can understand the way the horse moves, what feeling it gives, and therefore how it achieves what it does for their patients.

Other physiotherapists come with the riders from special schools or hospitals. Many give their time and skills voluntarily because they are interested in horses and riding as well as the benefits for the rider. Some go to all sessions, others can only go occasionally because of their workload and limited time. Each RDA region has a regional physiotherapist who is part of the regional team and most counties also have them now.[3]

The helper

The helper is one of the most important members of an RDA team. Without helpers, who give their time freely, the RDA would not exist. The instructor relies on the helper to make sure that the rider does not lose balance, that the rider is ready for any movement or change of pace, that the girth is tight and that the rider understands and obeys the instructor's commands. The physiotherapist relies on the helper to make sure that what they advise to help each rider is being carried out. The rider relies on the helper to help him improve in his horsemanship.

The helper should be trained and be made aware of how to lift, mount and dismount riders. They should know how to handle riders correctly both on and off the horse. The physiotherapist should also explain to the helpers the riders' problems and abilities, advising what to do to help and, just as important, what not to do.

Although helpers must only help the riders when it is necessary, they must be on hand at all times to prevent accidents from occurring; though allowing the rider as much independence as possible. In this way the helper gives the rider confidence, allowing him or her to gain the maximum benefit from each session.

Being a helper in a group is hard work. They

14 *Many helpers are needed when people with disabilities are riding. (Don Corcoran)*

have to attend regularly and on time. If they cannot attend then a dependable replacement should be found. They have to attend in all weathers and conditions. Often at the end of each session they are physically and mentally exhausted. Why do they do it? The answer to this is simple. They get a reward. Not any material thing, but something much more valuable; the satisfaction of knowing that they have helped others, whose normal capabilities may be limited by crutches or wheelchairs, to achieve things which are often the most important things in their lives. The pleasure of watching progress made and difficulties overcome compensates for many trivial discomforts and time spent.

Helpers should be **physically fit**, within reason. They should have many of the qualities applying to instructors. Thus, they must have empathy towards children and an appreciation of their abilities. Although having prior knowledge of horses is an advantage, it is not essential. Many excellent helpers have little previous knowledge (**14**).

How is the team selected?

An **instructor** in an RDA group must comply with the requirements of the RDA. An instructor should only be appointed after consultation with an RDA county chairman with advice from the regional or county instructor (see Chapter 9). Any person who wishes to instruct at an RDA group should first attend regular sessions of an RDA group recommended by the county or regional chairman or instructor before taking up the appointment.

The standard required of an instructor is of British Horse Society Preliminary Teaching Test Standard. The instructor need not necessarily take this examination but his ability to teach must be up to this standard. The instructor should be familiar with the RDA handbook, Pony Club manual of horsemanship and the British Horse Society instructors' handbook with special reference to the chapter on instructing beginners and the very young.

It is important for instructors to attend a regional or national RDA instructors' course before the group in which they wish to teach is considered for full membership of the RDA.

It is a basic requirement for running an RDA group to enlist a **physiotherapist** or **occupational therapist** willing to advise and assist at regular intervals. Physiotherapists who are members of the ACPRD are sometimes from other professions. To enhance the work of the instructor and help the helpers, the physiotherapist needs to be an integral part of the team. Physiotherapy has developed into a series of specialities which involve post-graduate training. Those involved in the RDA are striving to obtain a deeper knowledge and expertise in this area of therapy. The ACPRD works in close liaison with the RDA. The physiotherapists involved in RDA groups are responsible to their own professional body, the Chartered Society of Physiotherapy, yet they still need to be closely linked with the RDA to achieve the joint aims of both organizations.

Many **helpers** are needed to conduct a safe and successful therapeutic riding group. The number of helpers needed depends of course on the size and type of riding group being conducted, but there is no doubt that the helper is the true heart beat of any riding group.

Helpers can be of any shape or size, although they should be over 14 years old. They must have one thing in common; that is, to want to help others. Some helpers are students from schools, colleges and universities. They may come to help out as part of an equestrian-based course, in which case they might receive academic credit for their involvement in this activity, or they may come in free periods or in their spare time. Other helpers may come from youth clubs, such as the young farmers, scouting and guide organizations or any other type of club. Often helpers are mums, who come and help when their own children are at school, or they may be mothers of the riders.

Advertisements in the local newspaper or postcards in shop windows and libraries often attract helpers. Helpers have been obtained in the past from riding clubs, pony clubs, local riding schools, technical colleges, teacher training centres, schools and sixth-form colleges, university students, police cadets, borstal institutions, women's institutes, local service clubs and townswomen's guilds, appeals through local radio and television, adverts in local papers and parish magazines, pulpit appeals, notices in doctors', dentists', and vets' waiting rooms, pubs etc. . . .

Some people may be willing to help, but lack transport. In these cases it is often very difficult to arrange transport, although since helpers are very valuable everything is done to try and arrange transport for them.

An excellent place for recruiting helpers is at local pony and riding clubs. The riders are already experienced in horsemanship and know how to lead correctly.

Numbers needed, numbers involved

The RDA analysis of group census returns made by RDA groups in 1989 showed that there were 24,581 disabled riders and drivers of whom 16,244 were under 18 years of age. There were 688 groups offering riding and/or driving in Great Britain and a further 38 overseas and affiliated members of the RDA.

In approximate terms there are 1000 instructors, 300 physiotherapists and 13,300 voluntary helpers involved in RDA groups. Many of the groups split their session into two or more groups to enable them to cope with more riders. In this way safety is maintained as there are always the correct amount of helpers with an individual at any one time. About 35 per cent of riders are physically handicapped with mentally handicapped riders making up the other 65 per cent. Some riders require a leader and two side helpers whilst others may only require a leader and one side helper or even just a leader. In this way also,

a group which only has five ponies can cope with ten riders in any one session.

In 1989 the survey of groups registered by NARHA in the United States recorded approximately 22,000 riders with disabilities, predominately under the age of 18. There is no data regarding which disabilities are represented, or how many riders represent which disabilities.

Understanding the importance of co-operation

Considerable attention and effort should be spent in finding, training and retaining good helpers, but what could be a better or more rewarding way for an individual to spend the time given? Out of doors, with children and animals, in a healthy, happy environment, where the rewards are instant and many – joyful riders, enthusiastic parents/teachers/physiotherapists, and wonderful, friendly horses.

Whilst almost any individual may serve as a helper in a riding group, it is up to the instructor and group leaders to place the applying helper in a suitable position (15). For example, it is not necessary for a helper to have horse experience to be a successful contributor to the group. Applicants with horse experience can be used to prepare the horses for riding, lead the horses in the riding session, or to keep up the training level of the horse, or re-train the riding horse for its new role, if they are experienced in this area. Helper applicants without prior experience might be placed in less horse-related tasks at the outset and, as experience is gained, they may wish to join in more equestrian activities.

In the United States, helpers are required to complete three forms upon entering a riding group for the disabled.

1 **A helper information form,** which determines if the person has any medical problems which might influence their participation in the group. This form also requests information about any special hobbies or skills the person may have that would be beneficial to the riding group.

15 *Trained helpers demonstrating the correct leader and side helper positions.*

2 A medical emergency treatment form, so that in case of accident or injury at the riding group, the helper may get emergency medical help.

3 A liability form, freeing the group and its personnel from liability in case of an accident.

The most important part of helper participation in the riding group is training. **Training** is the key to providing the helper with guidelines for a good work experience. Even though this individual may be volunteering his or her time, the worker should consider him or herself a professional.

Conducting successful helper training

Group leaders often prepare a helper training manual/handbook, which includes the most important information that each helper should know. This manual includes a very brief history of riding for the disabled and the specific mission of the specific group for which the individual will be working. It describes in general terms the different helper positions available to the individual. It describes the desired behaviour of helpers, and perhaps outlines non-desirable behaviour, such as being too talkative, or overly helpful. It gives helpful hints on dealing with individuals who are disabled. It gives brief descriptions of the disabilities seen in the group, the major goals for riding and some methods of handling each disability. It contains information on mounting and dismounting students. It discusses in detail the correct way to lead a horse and the correct way to assist the mounted student. It contains information on what to do in case of an emergency. It outlines the schedule of the riding group, addressing the attendance requirements of helpers. It contains the phone numbers of appropriate people to contact in case of emergency, cancellation, weather conditions and the like. A well-organized, properly prepared helper manual is a great asset to a riding group. Every helper should receive this document and be encouraged not only to read it, but also to review it from time to time.

No helper should be put into service without proper training. It is not a good idea, if a group comes up short-handed on a given day, to recruit a willing but uneducated bystander. Helpers should be trained before participating in a group, and should receive regular update training as a part of their continuing participation in a riding group. This will make them feel prepared and qualified for their participation.

What does a helper training programme consist of?

While there is no required format in Great Britain or the United States, there are guidelines for such training provided in the handbook of the North American Riding for the Handicapped Association (NARHA) and training of this kind is provided throughout the many groups in Great Britain and the United States. The regime should be as follows:

1 An introduction: including the structure and objectives of the group. Present a brief overview of the disabilities accepted into the group, and a brief overview of the goals for each.

2 A tour of the facilities: starting with the car park, the rest rooms, tack room, stable area, introduce the group horses, riding arena, telephone with emergency instructions posted beside it, first aid supplies and the lights. Explain the operation of mechanical or technical devices and the like.

3 Display and explain all special equipment that might be used in the group, including special stirrups, hard hats and safety belts. Demonstrate how each is adjusted and let the trainees practice these activities.

4 Explain and demonstrate horse handling: start with catching the horse in the field and in the stable. Show how to tie up correctly, how to groom and how to tack up. Stress safety issues.

5 Proceed to the riding area and demonstrate the correct way to lead a horse. Explain what is needed at the halt, in walk, trot and in transitions.

6 Demonstrate mounting and dismounting methods and techniques. Specify the helper's role in each procedure and let each trainee gain experience by practising what has been demonstrated.

7 Explain and demonstrate handling techniques to be used with each handicapped rider. Using role playing, illustrate what to do in the following situations:
a) arrival and departure of students
b) inside the stable area, inside the riding area
c) during mounting and dismounting
d) during the riding lesson
e) during exercises and games

8 Conduct a mock lesson, or have trainees watch regular riding lessons. Make sure that this demonstration contains all the correct 'how-tos' since many people imitate what they see.

9 Then, conduct a practice session. Enough time must be allowed for each trainee to practise his or her newly learned skills. This is a very important phase of training. Use this time to make sure that leaders and side helpers are familiar and comfortable with their assigned roles. It is suggested that non-horse people be assigned as side helpers

only. Experienced equestrians should be used as horse leaders, since they understand how to handle the horse in a particular situation.

Throughout this part of the training, helpers must know exactly what is expected of them. Safety should be emphasized throughout. Correct handling methods should also be emphasized, so that no medical harm will be done to the rider as a result of incorrect handling techniques.

10 Discussion is the next part of the training programme. Make sure that the following topics are emphasized:

● Safety rules, including procedures in case of an accident or emergency.

● Appropriate clothing (depending on the climate). Each helper should be dressed comfortably with appropriate footwear.

● Promptness, regularity, reliability and commitment are all needed. The success of each rider in the group depends on these qualities.

● The role of the helpers in relation to the group and in the riding lesson. Each trainee should leave with a clear idea of his or her job.

● Attitudes and reactions to handicapped people. Explain the philosophy of the group and the relationship that could be developed between rider and helper. Allow time for negative as well as positive reactions. Try to give the trainees the idea that they can discuss their feelings with you at appropriate times and let them know that this work is not for everyone. Add that it is all right to resign if they become too heavily involved.

● Discuss additional helper opportunities available that are not related to the actual riding/vaulting/driving session.

11 Give the trainees time to consider if they are truly interested in participating. Give them helper forms to complete and a helper manual to take home to study. Suggest assignments.

12 Thank the trainees – the most essential ingredient of the training session. Helpers need to feel appreciated and wanted. They need to be recognized for the valuable help they give. They need to understand the importance of their jobs.

The work of helpers

What are some of the jobs and tasks in a riding group that helpers perform?

The most obvious are as **horse leader** and **side helper**, but there are a wide variety of other duties that can be tackled, such as **horse preparation**, including grooming, tacking up, exercising and training, and stable care and maintenance. Helpers can assist with **building projects**, such as a mounting ramp or a mounting block. Helper co-ordinators can make sure that the right number of trained helpers are on hand. Help can be given with **special events**, such as a demonstration day or horse show or fund raising effort. Helpers can prepare **group publicity** and public relations information. There is really no limit to what helpers can do. The key to their successful participation is in proper training and correct placement.

Helpers are encouraged to give feedback about their assignment and their students. In fact, many helpers are actively involved in **student assessment**, keeping brief records on their riders' progress, or the lack of it, and problems or other situations that might affect their positive participation in the riding group. Helpers enjoy being involved in staff discussions about how to work with more difficult students. Their input is invaluable to instructors designing individual rider educational programmes.

Helpers are also encouraged to attend local, county/state, regional and national conferences and in the United States continuing education courses sponsored by local educational institutions. This helps to ensure that the quality of their participation is maintained. It is also a way of expressing appreciation for their commitment to the movement of riding for the disabled; its groups, instructors, other helpers and most of all its riders in Great Britain, the United States and all over the world.

MY FRIEND – MY HORSE

Horse and rider relationships

David is a small child who has cerebral palsy. The highlight of his week is his visit to the riding stables and his ride on Bubbles, his best friend. When he is mounted, excitement radiates from him; the smile shows all. His mount, Bubbles, is quite happy to give him a ride. He will walk through the poles and trot happily along, because when it comes to the end of the session there is a

16 *What joy! (Diamond Riding Centre)*

big hug in store for him and he is made much of. David is usually a quiet child who can barely walk unaided, yet after his riding session he wants to tell the world of his achievements. The affection he has for his four-legged friend shines in his face. Mrs Van Otterllo sums up the effect horses have on the handicapped so well:

> If you look at the happy faces of these children it is not difficult to imagine what joy this form of physiotherapy brings them, mainly because for them it is no treatment at all, but one of the loveliest sports they can do. And how they love their physiotherapist, their horse, because a horse is warm and big and strong, it provides them with four healthy legs, it can be touched and stroked and brushed and cleaned and fed as well as ridden, and that is much more than any physiotherapist can offer (16).

It is easy to see why horses mean so much to riders with disabilities, they are their best friends, just as a guide dog is a blind person's best friend. The guide dog helps the blind person to live as normal a life as possible, enabling the owner to get out and about. A horse can not only restore a disabled person's mobility but can also provide him with a feeling of **freedom** and **independence**. Perhaps the only time a disabled person can experience this is while he is on horseback.

A rider with disabilities can form a partnership with a pony, establishing a bond which is theirs alone. They achieve things together and they fall short of their goals together, but it is a shared experience.

Individuals who have disabilities tend to be very protected in their normal environments. They are not allowed to experience any sense of risk or danger. When they ride horses, there can be a chance of the unexpected which they often find stimulating. This brings forth new feelings in them, which leads to a new inner awareness of themselves and more often than not better communication with the people around them.

Can horses read thoughts?

Ponies are said to have a sixth sense. They certainly seem to be aware of having someone on their back who needs to be treated sensitively. A pony who walks sedately around a school, listening to the instructor's voice and acting intuitively, will, with an experienced rider on its back, often be extremely lively and full of fun out on a hack. Ponies need to be allowed to let off steam in this way if they are to be kept healthy in body and mind. A happy pony serves the disabled rider the best.

A pony's intelligence must never be misjudged. However, whether his ability to motivate his rider, which is one of his most useful attributes, is accomplished knowingly or unknowingly is always cause for debate.

Ponies do communicate through body language. We must interpret what they are trying to say and put things right. For instance, when a pony misbehaves for no apparent reason, we should not assume that he is being naughty, for he may be in discomfort or even pain. A pony that suddenly starts to buck may have a rider who is sitting too heavily on his back, or he may be developing a saddle sore. These things are communicated to humans through body language. There is always a reason for a problem suddenly developing.

A new pony will often play up or may take advantage of a nervous rider. How does he know that his rider is nervous? The answer always given is that he can sense it. Ponies in RDA groups do have to go through a rigorous selection and training process, to allow them, amongst other things, to get used to riders who are either nervous or worried. When an experienced pony senses these emotions in a rider, he is often seen to act very quietly and sensibly. Helpers are often heard to say, 'He knows.'

Suitable horses and ponies

There are many things to be taken into consideration, when choosing suitable mounts; for the group initially, and then for the individual riders. The ponies should not be just 'acquired', they should be *selected*. Indeed, they should be very carefully selected by people with a sound knowledge of horses, who are also familiar with the needs of handicapped riders and appropriate qualities in ponies. A veterinary surgeon must also give the pony a clean bill of health. It is always important to try to obtain the past medical records of any animal being donated or purchased for therapeutic riding. Such records will prove invaluable in assessing the suitability of the animal for its new work. To be acceptable for RDA work the pony must fulfil many requirements.

Temperament

This is the first thing to consider when looking at a pony. Every pony used for disabled riders, must have a calm and kind temperament. If a pony bites or kicks he must be discounted immediately. A pony must be a *friend*. There is no place for bad behaviour of any kind in therapy groups. It may not be the pony's fault; he may have been mistreated; however, there is not the time to retrain such animals were this even possible.

Ponies which are high-spirited rarely settle to

this special work and can be unpredictable. This should not be confused with a pony who is initially frisky, yet settles to his work well. This is a sign of good health. On the other hand the pony which is sluggish or appears lifeless is of no real value either. He must be forward and straight-moving with a happy outlook. He must lead easily and rhythmically, be willing to carry out his duties, and stand perfectly still when required.

His character must also be evaluated. Cheeky should not be interpreted as naughty. A cheeky pony may do his work extremely well. All well and good if he enjoys life, as long as he carries out his duties willingly: he may provide inspiration for the riders. A pony which does not have any apparent character of his own does not help his rider to form a bond and consequently does not motivate his rider.

Age

The age of the pony plays an important role in the selection process. Generally ponies under five years of age are underdeveloped and inexperienced, whilst older ponies should be very carefully vetted for soundness. Between five and fifteen is usually the best age for ponies that are to work in RDA groups. Young ponies may seem to be well-trained and sensible; however, they do tend to be unpredictable. All ponies need reminders of how to behave from time to time and should be ridden regularly by competent and able riders.

Predictability is often a quality which comes only with maturity. However, older ponies are also a risk. They may become tired easily or become stiff and possibly start to stumble. An old pony in its late twenties may have severe joint problems, resulting in poor quality of movement. This animal would not be suitable, since the basis for therapy using the pony is related to its quality of movement. Ponies in the ideal age bracket are often the easiest to maintain. They should only be accepted into the RDA group if they are in

excellent health and thereafter should be maintained at that level.

Size range

The ponies most often used in RDA work are from between 12 and 15.2 hands high. Smaller ponies or larger horses can be useful for certain riders, but are not usually suitable for the majority. They all have to be fed and looked after properly and it may not be a viable proposition to keep one pony for just one certain rider. Some groups may only cater for either adults or children or some may cater for both. The size and 'fit' of the horse or pony to the riders who will receive therapy on the animal is of great importance (17).

17 *A small pony and a large horse, both of which can be used for riders with disabilities.*

Size is not always an indicator of weight-carrying ability. A stocky 13-hand pony may be capable of carrying as much weight as a larger but finer horse. We are very lucky in the UK to have so many stocky native breeds, who seem to adapt to RDA work very easily. Sturdy cobs of about 15 hands high and the larger native breeds are all quite capable of carrying most adults.

However, height is not the only thing to consider; conformation and width are also important. A range of ponies with wide and narrow backs and chests are useful to have, as are short- and long-backed animals. A narrow-backed animal is needed initially for a rider with cerebral palsy, who has tight muscles inside the thigh (adduction), if he is to be able to sit astride comfortably. Some of the ponies with wide backs are useful for riders who lack balance (18). It is most important for each rider to be matched correctly with each pony. It is also extremely important for each pony to be matched with its

helper. The small helpers will not be able to assist the rider who is sitting on top of a big horse. New helpers may also be a little anxious when leading larger horses and this of course does not do either the helper, the horse or the rider any good.

Gait

The gait of each pony will be determined by its conformation. Whether the mount is large or small, he should be freely moving forward at each pace. In general a pony that has **correct conformation** will provide a smooth, balanced ride. Each pace should be well defined with regular beats. The transition from one pace to another should be smooth, without the leader needing to pull at the pony's head (19).

The gait and movement of each pony will affect the improvement of disability in each rider; for instance, a smooth-gaited pony may be necessary at first for a paralysed rider. A pony with a definite beat can often help in achieving

19 *This pony has very poor conformation. It is unlikely that she will provide a smooth balanced ride, and would, therefore, be unsuitable for use in an RDA group.*

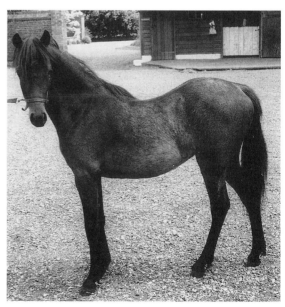

18 *A wide pony is useful for a rider who lacks balance.*

the rising trot. A calm pony may aid a hyper-active rider and a more active pony may stimulate the slower rider.

Most suitable type – is there one?

Is a perfect pony needed? The answer is yes, at least as perfect as possible. If enough time and effort is spent, then these mounts can be found.

The matter of whether to choose a mare or a gelding is a personal thing. Many people blame mares for being skittish when in season; however, if the mare works well at all other times there is no cause to dismiss her. Mares are often said to be more perceptive than geldings where disabled riders are concerned. All animals have mood swings at times and if a mare does turn a little silly when in season then a replacement should be used for those particular sessions.

It is impossible to say if there is one breed which makes the best pony for RDA work. As said before, the native UK breeds do seem to settle to the work very well, although of course there are exceptions. It should not be assumed that because it is a native breed it will do the work well. If you go around the various RDA groups you will find ponies of all different breeds. Some use breeds local to their particular area, such as Welsh Mountain and New Forest. There are also many ponies in groups which could be entered into a 'spot the breed' competition, that do the

20 The perfect pony? This pony is certainly a 'good sort' and has proved himself to be a valuable member of 'The Magpie Group'.

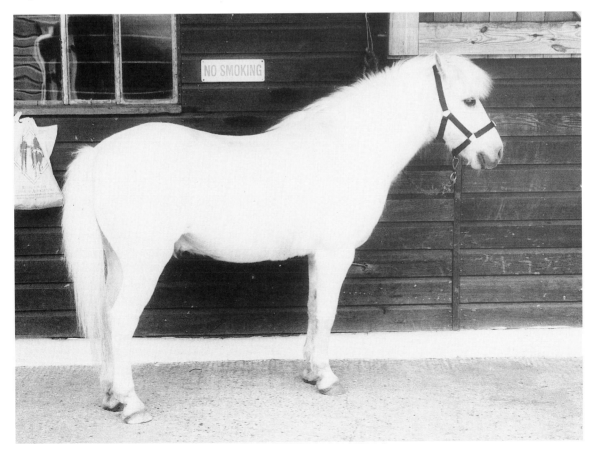

job equally as well. Groups have been known to use Arabs and Thoroughbreds with success, although it should be pointed out that these are generally the exception to the rule (**20**).

While many breed organizations purport to have the perfect therapeutic riding pony and state the reasons for such claims, in fact, no breed is preferable above any other. Any pony is a potential candidate for RDA work. The points discussed in selecting the right pony and its training, will eventually prove whether it actually is the most suitable type.

Accepting that there are not enough perfect ponies to go around, notice must be taken of individual faults, idiosyncrasies, likes and dis-likes, and tact used to get the best out of each pony.

In conclusion, all of the ponies, whether large or small, mares or geldings, grey or black, should at the end of the day have done their work well. They will then become a mutual friend of the whole RDA team.

Requirements from the start

Once a pony is deemed suitable for use in disabled riding programmes, that is to say, fulfils all of the aforementioned requirements, it will need to go through a process of training. We must assume that the pony has already been bitted, backed, ridden regularly by competent riders and in general been handled with care. It is most important to start with a pony which is free from vice and has not been muddled up in some way by its previous owner. It is much more difficult to try to re-train a pony which has had bad training and it is nearly impossible to correct major vices. As much of the pony's history must be sought as possible. If he has had any bad experiences in the past, he *will* remember them and shy away from any thing associated with them in the future.

Riding school ponies make excellent recruits for RDA groups. They are already used to being ridden regularly by both competent riders and beginners. They will have been taught to walk, trot and canter quietly. They will be used to clumsy beginners and to a regular routine. Whether the pony is a school pony or not, it is important that it is regularly ridden by compet-ent riders during its training and throughout its career in RDA work. It must be started in the way it will have to carry on and must be maintained at the level. Developing faults must be corrected before they get worse. The pony should be kept supple, obedient and interested in his work. Regular hacks and different activities with able-bodied riders will help to keep the pony happy.

Who owns the horses and ponies?

Groups which have their own facilities may own their own ponies, they may have ponies lent to them, or they may borrow ponies for single sessions at a time or for longer periods. In the case of group ownership the ponies' upkeep will be the responsibility of the group. The RDA advises that a group must ensure, before contem-plating ownership of ponies, that it has sufficient knowledge, suitable facilities, adequate financial resources and enough experienced and knowledgeable manpower to take on the re-sponsibility and to maintain proper care. There must be a person in charge, who can make decisions on his own and follow them through in emergencies. In all other cases consultation with other members of the group is desirable. The person in charge, usually the instructor, must be available at all times.

The RDA states that it has a duty to look after the ponies it owns and to set a required standard for those it hires or borrows. Many ponies are offered to RDA groups throughout the year for loan or as a gift. Unfortunately, many are unsuitable. Some may be too old or do not fulfil the group's requirements. Groups are always cautious before accepting a pony as a gift. It still has to go through the same selection process as any other pony. In a situation where a pony is not suitable, the owner should be handled very carefully, so as not to upset his feelings or cause offence. It might be pointed out that although the pony is very nice, it is not suitable because of the needs of disabled riders. The group may then be instrumental in helping to find a suitable home if that is required.

If a pony is acceptable, then it should be examined by a veterinary surgeon before the group finally accepts it. The vet will be able to make sure that it is in good health and can stand up to the work. It is also advisable to set a trial period, to give the pony a chance to settle to the work.

Loaning of ponies can become a tricky business. Where a pony is put up for loan to an RDA group a contract should be made clearly stating the terms. The length of the loan should also be made clear. Any points specific to that pony must be stated. If the pony needs emergency treatment the owners must give their consent for the instructor to act as he sees fit. The contract should cover where the pony is to be kept and by whom it will be used, as far as possible. It should also state who is responsible for any necessary veterinary attention and for the pony's insurance. The RDA has an agreement form for the gift of horses or ponies to the RDA which is available from headquarters.

Groups which own their own ponies must not hire them out for payment to the general public. This would be acting illegally, even if it were in an attempt to raise funds. To do this, the group would need to apply for a riding school licence and in view of the charitable status of the RDA, headquarters would need to be consulted.

Ponies which are loaned by private owners can be freely used within the group so long as no hiring fee is being charged. There is, however, no objection to travelling expenses being reimbursed to the owners.

If a pony is offered for loan to a group which does not need him, he can be put on a central register at the RDA headquarters if the donor wishes. Then if another group requests such a pony, he may, with the owner's permission, be transferred to that group.

Where a riding school and its ponies are used by an RDA group, it is the policy of the RDA to encourage groups to raise funds to pay for the hiring of the facilities and the use of ponies. Many riding school proprietors are very generous and do not expect payment; however, they should not be taken for granted. The group should be run in a professional way, with as businesslike a manner as possible.

It is the usual situation in the United States to acquire horses or ponies for therapeutic riding by donation. This donation by a given individual is tax-deductible, and is therefore a financial benefit to the donor. The therapeutic riding group accepting the donated horse or pony must first have obtained a favourable ruling from the Internal Revenue Service as a charitable organization, thus allowing it to accept such a donation. The owner of the animal, not the therapeutic riding group, decides for tax purposes the value of the gift animal. The programme need only give the owners a letter stating that the animal has been received as a donation to the programme. These donated animals are sometimes a mixed blessing, however. The gift animal may be too old and infirm to be of any therapeutic value. Other animals may be donated because the owner has outgrown them, or the seller feels that the value of the donation exceeds the price he might receive for selling the animal. In each case, as long as the animal is evaluated thoroughly, as in RDA groups in the UK, then its value, in relation to the specific needs of the therapeutic riding group accepting the donated animal, can be assessed.

Once the animal has been deemed useful to the specific programme, a formal agreement should be drawn up as in the UK; however, it is very important in this instance to include liability and what measures will be taken should the animal prove unsuitable. This agreement should also state that the animal has become the sole property of the therapeutic riding group and that when it becomes unusable, the programme may dispose of the animal in any way it deems suitable.

In addition to horses and ponies that are donated, therapeutic riding groups, as with RDA groups in the UK, have the option to purchase an animal, or lease an animal. In each case, however, it is advisable to have an agreement between the seller or lessor and the therapeutic riding programme. This agreement will state the specific terms of the sale or lease, and will be signed by the parties involved.

Horses' upkeep – sponsor schemes

Once a pony has been purchased by a group, it is then the group's responsibility to feed it, make sure it has the necessary stabling and grazing and that its farriery and veterinary needs are met. The group must plan and be responsible for its own finances, including keeping a reserve for any unforeseen eventuality.

The pony must be wormed regularly and vaccinated against influenza and tetanus. There is a vaccine scheme, whereby for a number of years vaccine for animals used in RDA work has been supplied by four of the major pharmaceutical companies. The scheme is designed for animals whose owners are 'genuinely unable to afford vaccination'.

Ponies used for RDA work which are commercial riding school ponies will not be covered by the scheme. Ponies owned by the RDA and used solely for RDA work will. There is of course a lot of variation within the scheme. Where ponies are

travelling to shows they will be required to have had the correct vaccinations.

One way in which groups can help finance their scheme is by involving sponsors and/or adopters of ponies or riders. Many local firms, pubs or clubs will agree to sponsor a pony or rider for a term or year if approached in the right way. Members of the public may like to sponsor a pony. They can receive photographs and news of their pony and should of course be able to come and see it.

A Horse, Of Course!

by Jean M. Tebay

Oh horse, you are a wondrous thing,
No buttons to push, no engine that pings.
You start yourself, no clutch to slip,
No dead battery, no gears to strip.
No licence buying every year,
With plates to screw on front and rear.
No gas fumes polluting the air each day,
Taking the joys of nature away.
No speed cops dashing into view,
Writing a ticket out to you.
Your super-treads all seem OK,
And hoofpick in hand, they should stay that way.
Your spark plugs never miss a cue,
Your motor never makes us stew,
Your frame is good for many a mile,
Your body never outdates its style.
Your needs are few, and happily met,
We honour you, we're in your debt!
You serve us well, as our riders you carry,
Making instructors, helpers – the whole team
*   merry.*

Yes, horse, you are a wondrous thing,
Teacher – Therapist – Friend, your praises we
*   sing!*

4 TRAINING OF HORSES AND PONIES

Starting with the right ones

We have already discussed how important it is to start with the right type of pony. Therefore, we must assume that the pony fulfils all of the RDA group's requirements and that it is free from vice and does not have any problems. This includes making sure that the pony does not have a serious illness or disease. Ponies which are unsound in wind or limb should not be used by the group. A handicapped rider does not need a handicapped horse.

Once it has been decided that the pony is in good health and is as near perfect as possible for the job in hand, its training for RDA work can begin. The RDA stresses that, 'All new ponies must be thoroughly tested by an able-bodied rider under the group's normal riding conditions *before* a rider with disabilities is allowed to mount.'

Acclimatizing horses and ponies

Once the pony arrives at the stable yard where he is to be kept, he should be left to settle in. If he seems nervous and would be likely to gallop about if turned out he should be kept in a stable for a day. If there is a quiet pony that he could be turned out with, and the newcomer seems sensible, he will probably benefit from being allowed to graze. After he has been at the yard for a few days he should be wormed and given his vaccinations if these are not up to date.

Once he has settled into the routine of the yard and seems quite happy, it is time for training to begin.

The pony will already have been handled correctly and ridden by a competent rider, therefore it is not the normal training of a pony that needs to be considered, but the special training that he must receive to maximize his usefulness for the group. The main thing to remember when starting with a new pony is never to rush him. It is much better to take a little longer, getting the desired result in the end. If the pony is rushed, he may reject new things and rebel against what he is being asked to do. Most ponies will accept new things at their own pace. Many trainers use a system of punishment and reward. If punishment is to be given, it must be administered directly an incident has occurred and similarly with reward, directly the pony has accepted something new.

The first thing to do is to get the pony used to his place of work. Presumably this will be an enclosed area, for the safety of the riders. Let the pony loose in this area so that he can explore the hidden corners and become acquainted with the monsters lurking there! The pony will settle on his own far more quickly than if he were being led around. Once he has settled catch him again and put him back in his stable.

The next session should be a ridden one. The

instructor or an experienced rider should take the pony to the work area and get the feel of him. All of his good points and bad points should be noted. Once the pony has been returned to his stable, the rider should make a programme for correcting any faults the pony might have. These should only be minor and a few training sessions should begin to see an improvement. Whilst training, the pony should be given as much variety in his work as possible, to keep him happy in his work.

When the trainer is satisfied that the pony is light to handle, will stand quite still when being mounted and dismounted and makes smooth transitions from one pace to another, it is time to get him used to different things he will encounter within an RDA session.

What aids are acceptable?

The aids are the **communication** from rider to horse. When riding, the seat, legs, hands and voice are used to control the pony. Able-bodied riders have the potential to develop all of these aids in turn and so become competent riders. Individuals with disabilities may lack the potential to develop these aids due to their disability. For instance, an amputee may lack one or both of his legs or arms. Within the extremes of these riders, there are riders who have arms and legs, but cannot control them in the correct way. In short, there are many, many disabilities which hinder riders, yet there are also many individuals who can develop their potential to become competent riders by compensating one of the more usual aids with one that has been proved to work for them and is accepted by the properly trained pony.

Many disabilities make the application of leg aids very difficult or even impossible. In cases where the rider's muscles are very tight or are affected by spasm, a programme of exercises which make the rider use these muscles will help the muscles relax. This will benefit the rider's legs and will enable him to use leg aids to some degree. It is often found that riders who cannot use leg aids develop stronger muscles in other areas: their seat for example. Rather than using the lower leg to push the pony forward the rider thrusts strongly forward with his seat and so communicates forward rhythmic movement to the pony.

If the rider has some ability to utilize the aids, even if only in a small way, then he should be encouraged to learn to ride in the normal way. If, however, the rider is restricted due to his disability, then the instructor should seek the therapists help as to what **compensation** should be encouraged. John Anthony Davies explains how compensation works: 'Compensating aids are the means by which the rider uses, or develops for use, a stronger or fitter part of the body, or a limb to take over, or assist a weaker or less effective part.'

The aids which a rider may develop may be rather unorthodox, yet he should be encouraged to use them if it results in him being able to make the pony understand what is required, and so ride. Compensation should not be allowed if it is only to make the rider's job a little easier. If a rider is capable of producing the normal aids to any degree, even if he does find it difficult, he should be encouraged to develop the normal aids to the best of his ability. This will not, however, be carried to the extreme of distressing the rider. Careful evaluation of the situation and constant assessment is needed to avoid frustration leading to the rider giving up.

Artificial aids, such as riding sticks, are accepted by the pony, yet the rider must be able to use them properly and in conjunction with the aids, normal or compensated, which are used.

The voice must play a large part in the communication between pony and rider. Ponies which respond to the voice will often walk on at the right command or stop when requested by voice. Voice response is an important part of the RDA ponies' training. Once certain words, such as 'walk on' or 'halt', are keyed the desired result can be achieved by the rider, even if he cannot transmit his intentions through other means.

Breaking in

Ordinarily, the term 'breaking in' applies to young horses or ponies being trained and ridden for the first time. When relating to riding for the disabled, the term 'breaking in' usually applies to the pony being trained or re-trained and acclimatized to new equipment. Very few groups have the facilities or the time to bring in youngsters and break them solely for the purpose of disabled riding. This would be an excellent way of ensuring the ponies were trained correctly from the start, solely for RDA, but would take far too long until the pony could be used reliably and safely.

The specialized training required is all that needs to be discussed in this chapter. There are many excellent books on breaking and training youngsters in the normal way and it is of course presumed that any RDA pony has had sound basic formal training.

Keeping the pony's attention

The pony's attention must be kept on the job in hand at all times. Whether he is being trained to new equipment, being hacked out or in a lesson, he must be alert and responsive. When ponies start to lose their concentration accidents can occur. They can become clumsy and start to trip.

The pony's routine whilst being trained and ridden should be as varied as possible. Hacks, jumping and lungeing should all be integrated with the normal RDA sessions. *A happy pony serves the disabled rider best.*

Short sharp commands are often a good way of making sure the pony understands what you are trying to communicate to him. Lots of little niggling commands make the pony switch off. A clear aid, given either physically or with the voice, keeps the pony's concentration on his work.

Variation within sessions keeps the pony fresh and enjoying his work. Games played, music, and even races can be as enjoyable for the pony as for the rider. Ponies do seem to enjoy certain aspects of RDA work. Of course nobody would like to think that the ponies were doing their work under protest, after all they are the most important factor of the whole process. It is nice to think that they are enjoying their work and doing it willingly.

Getting mounts used to special equipment

There are many peculiar things a pony will need to become accustomed to. Some of the most

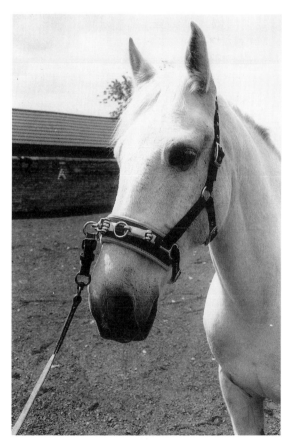

21 *A lungeing cavesson is an essential piece of equipment when training horses.*

important things he must accept are: wheelchairs which are empty, or have people in them and are moving; people using crutches, which may be dropped and crash to the ground; mounting blocks of all shapes and sizes; mounting ramps, with people in wheelchairs going up and down; people on the mounting ramps who will be higher than the pony's head and may seem extremely imposing; riders with braces, artificial legs, etc; many people around, helpers leaning over their backs assisting riders to mount; riders mounting clumsily; mounting, dismounting, and leading from both sides.

These are all things that the pony must learn to accept at his own pace. Patience is of the utmost importance when teaching the pony to accept things. No pony can be made to accept something until he has realized that it holds no danger. Reward is a great incentive to the pony.

When the pony is to encounter a new object, whatever it might be, he should first be allowed to inspect it. He may take one look and decide that it is of no more importance than a bale of straw. On the other hand, he may decide that there is a monster lurking somewhere and it may take him hours or days to accept it. Once a pony has truly accepted a new object, he will never again be frightened or worried about it. Time spent acclimatizing ponies to new things is time well spent.

Whenever a new object is introduced, the pony must be allowed to observe and inspect it whilst it is still and in motion if this is what he will encounter at riding sessions. Similarly, if the equipment is associated with people in it, or using it, such as wheelchairs and crutches, then able-bodied people must demonstrate it to the pony. In other words, the pony must accept all of these things as being *normal*, whatever the object or equipment, and however it is used. He should be reassured all of the time by voice and by patting and stroking him softly, showing him that there is nothing that is going to harm him. He must accept one lesson at a time. He should not be confused by introducing him to many differ-

ent things at once. When he has shown that he is not concerned about a certain object, then it is time to move on to the next.

'Little and often', applies to many things with horses. When training the pony to accept new things, this is a good rule to keep in mind. Under no circumstances should a pony be used in a riding session, which has not gone through a training process or accepted all new equipment and things asked of it. It is much better to find a new pony that will accept things, rather than make do with the one you have. However, in general there are few ponies that will not accept things required for disabled riding, given time.

Not only does the pony have to be broken to new equipment and different methods, but he also has to get used to different sensations and the feel of different things. Where a rider has no leg/s, he may use artificial leg/s. These feel totally different to a pony and the *feel* of them is something that the pony must accept. Riders without limbs obviously have problems in distributing their weight equally on both sides of the pony. The pony must therefore learn to react calmly to aids which might be given by a *hard* leg on one or both sides. He must also learn to keep moving straight, even when the rider's weight in the seat, being unequal, suggests otherwise.

An able-bodied rider should ride the horse and simulate as far as possible the difference in weight distribution by putting more weight in the stirrup on one side than the other and by using alternately hard aids on one side and soft aids on the other side. At first the pony may try to run away from, or evade the aids. With the help of a competent rider who will not allow him to get away with this, the pony should soon settle and take note of other aids such as the voice, and not act totally on an aid which feels *different*.

When the pony is indifferent to everything shown to him, as well as everything used on him, and responds to everything asked of him, then he can be mounted by a disabled rider and used in the lessons. A training schedule will be helpful when deciding whether a pony is ready to be used

HORSE TRAINING SCHEDULE SHEET

Horse's Name:_____

Trainer's Name:_____

Date Training Started: _____

Date Training Completed: _____

Areas completed in training:	Completed	Date
1 Accepts being led, both sides	[_____]	_____
2 Accepts side-helpers, both sides	[_____]	_____
3 Accepts rider movements	[_____]	_____
4 Accepts rider noises	[_____]	_____
5 Accepts ramp/mounting block	[_____]	_____
6 Accepts wheelchair on ground	[_____]	_____
7 Accepts wheelchair on ramp	[_____]	_____
8 Accepts wheelchair transfer	[_____]	_____
9 Accepts crutches, canes	[_____]	_____
10 Accepts balls, rings, games	[_____]	_____
11 Obeys voice command – halt	[_____]	_____
12 Obeys voice command – walk	[_____]	_____
13 Obeys voice command – trot	[_____]	_____
14 Obeys voice command – canter	[_____]	_____
15 Obeys halt command on lunge	[_____]	_____
16 Lunges both directions – walk	[_____]	_____
17 Lunges both directions – trot	[_____]	_____
18 Lunges both directions – canter	[_____]	_____
19 Performs smooth transitions, led	[_____]	_____
20 Performs smooth transitions on lunge	[_____]	_____
21 Accepts special adapted equipment	[_____]	_____

This animal has been reviewed and is ready for service in a therapeutic riding programme.

Signed (Evaluator)_____   Date Reviewed_____

---

22 Horse training schedule sheet (developed by Jean Tebay)

in a therapeutic riding lesson, especially if the trainer of the pony is not the instructor (**22**).

Lungeing – how it is of special importance to RDA ponies

When a horse is lunged, it wears a lungeing cavesson with three rings attached to the front of the noseband (**21**). A lunge line is then attached

51

to the cavesson. The trainer or instructor stands in the middle of the school and makes the pony go around the outside track, in a circle, by using his voice and a lungeing whip. The whip is never used on the pony, but is there to keep the pony moving forward.

Lungeing plays an important part in the training of RDA ponies for their new environment. The value of lungeing in training, re-training and exercising is emphasized by the RDA, but it also stresses that it must be done properly by someone who has learned the correct technique. Where vaulting is to be taught, much preparatory work must be done on a suitable pony before it is safe or suitable for use for this activity. One of the biggest benefits is the act of getting the pony to respond to the voice. *Walk on,*

whoa or *halt, stand* and *trot on,* are all sounds which the horse learns to recognize and act upon. The pony learns to take commands from the trainer, who in many cases is the instructor (**23**). This can be invaluable in lessons, when the instructor, by verbal commands, can help the rider to achieve the desired result; thus helping to improve the rider's confidence. Once the rider sees that the pony can and will do things for him, he will gain the incentive to *make* the pony do things.

The pony will also learn whether he is being rewarded or punished by the voice alone. *Good*

23 *Lungeing is of immense value when training, re-training, exercising and getting the horse to respond to voice commands.*

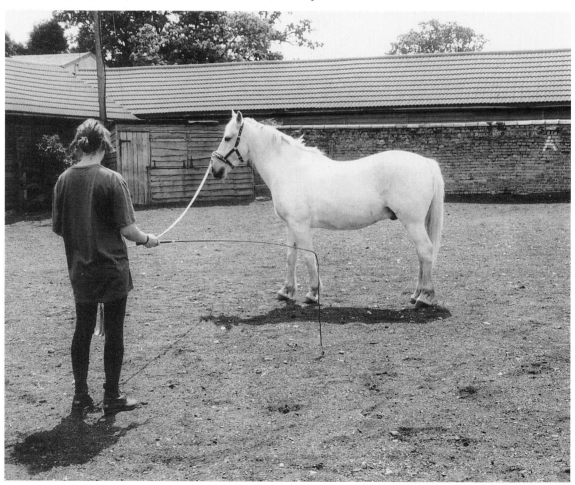

boy or a sharp *No* tells the pony whether his actions are correct or not. Most ponies are quick to learn to respond to the voice and in turn learn to anticipate the instructor's requirements.

Lungeing is also a useful way of allowing the pony to see and experience new things, without too much constraint. Strategically positioned equipment will allow the pony to see it but not get tangled up in it. He will learn to walk and trot past it without worrying. The sense of freedom a pony feels on the lunge does seem to produce results rather quicker than if he were being led, where the leader is acting as an influence on him.

24 *A headcollar is worn under the bridle to allow the pony to be controlled without interfering with the reins.*

Leaders and side-walkers should be introduced to the pony on the lunge. A nylon headcollar should be put under the bridle for a lead rein to be attached if and when necessary. The pony should get used to a leader leading from the headcollar, standing parallel with his shoulder, and one or two side-walkers, walking close to his sides (**24**). This can produce a claustrophobic feeling for the pony and is one more thing to be overcome. When the pony is used to the instructor standing in the middle, the leader and the side-walkers, it is time to introduce a rider. The rider must be an able-bodied rider, who can cope with any sudden reactions. The pony should get used to the rider being assisted by the side-walkers, which may entail having arms put across his back. He should also be taught to accept a rider being dragged from him. This is sometimes necessary for a variety of reasons.

Lungeing should make the pony obedient to the aids and voice commands and should help him to understand what is required of him, even if the rider seems to be communicating different commands from those of the instructor's verbal ones.

Ongoing training

However well trained a pony is, it is essential he be kept trained and not allowed to deteriorate or develop bad habits. All ponies used in groups and ridden regularly by riders with disabilities should be exercised frequently by competent riders. In this way a developing fault can be corrected, before it becomes a bad habit. The pony will also be provided with exercise and activity that will keep him supple and interested as well as obedient.

Feeding needs

All ponies are fed according to their weight and the work that they do. However, consideration should be given to the different types of work ponies are required to undertake. A show jumping pony obviously needs to have plenty of energy-giving food, whereas an RDA pony of the same weight cannot burn up the energy as quickly. Too much hard feed (corn and grain) should be avoided for RDA ponies. Generally a fresh supply of grass or good hay should provide enough energy for the work an RDA pony has to do. If the pony increases his work load and his work is more demanding then his feed can be increased accordingly .

The pony will soon let you know if his feed rations are correct. If he becomes too lively, then it is likely that he is being fed too much. If he appears listless then his feed should be increased; however, if you do not see a marked improvement there may be something medically wrong and a vet's opinion should be sought.

In general it is a better idea to work ponies off grass (turned out) than stabled, except where weather or surroundings prevent this.

Safety when training

Safety is the major aspect to be considered when training the pony. No exercises should be carried out if they could possibly put the trainer/ instructor, helpers or ponies at any risk. When training is being carried out, in whatever form, mounted or dismounted, there should always be helpers on hand to assist, should this be necessary.

To train ponies correctly, the tack used must be in excellent working order and it must fit the pony correctly. Only an experienced horse person should undertake the training of the pony for RDA work, and this individual should also have an understanding of basic RDA practices. The trainer must be able to demonstrate good judgement and be sensitive to the differing needs of the ponies.

Before the pony starts his training, the safety aspect should be thoroughly looked into. Some of the questions the trainer should think about are: Is the pony fit and well? Has he been wormed and

vaccinated? Are his feet correctly shod and kept in order? Does he seem happy? Is he being correctly fed and looked after? When the trainer is satisfied, he can begin the training programme set out for each pony confident that the pony is fit and healthy and quite capable of being trained well for his job.

If there were to be any problems, such as the pony losing shoes or becoming fatigued because of ill health, then his training could be set back for weeks.

Training for driving

Driving is an activity which is available to all disabled people, especially those who are physically or mentally incapable of riding, those who are too heavy to ride or just people who would benefit greatly from the experience.

The training of ponies for driving is a specialized area and should only be undertaken by an experienced driver. The term used for an experienced driver is a *whip*. Ponies being trained for driving also have to become familiar with special equipment. They will have to accept wheelchairs being wheeled up into the driving vehicle, or wheelchairs being loaded from a position level with the vehicle, which again may seem quite imposing to the new pony.

Ponies from 11.2 hh to 13.2 hh are ideal but there are exceptions. It is recommended that RDA vehicles are used in driving groups. Information on these can be obtained from the RDA headquarters.

Safety is of extreme importance with driving groups. It is not advisable to take drivers with disabilities out on public roads. However, some groups who have experienced driving helpers will take drivers with disabilities on known quiet routes to increase the feeling of freedom and independence. Convoy drives on private roads and tracks, instructional drives and obstacle driving are recommended.

Without handicapped drivers present, the new

pony must be put through a series of training sessions to familiarize it with the correct use of special equipment. There must be an experienced able-bodied whip, preferably the owner or usual driver of the pony, present at all training sessions.

Good-quality harness is essential. It must be suitable for the pony it is used on, in good repair, safe, clean and it must fit correctly.

Vaulting

Vaulting is an increasingly common activity within the broad spectrum of RDA. Vaulting is where the rider may physically leap onto the horse from the ground and perform gymnastics on horseback. Many disabled riders will be incapable of trying this activity. Selection must take in to consideration the age, riding ability and physical and mental ability of the individual.

This is a specialized area where the pony needs to be specially trained for the job, rather than just accepting different things. Mounts for this activity should stand between 14 hh and 15.2 hh. They need to be very responsive to the voice, well trained on the lunge, and show smooth transitions from one pace to another. All of the pony's paces should be forward-moving, keeping a well balanced rhythm at each pace. The mounts should be well rounded with broad backs and low withers.

Special equipment is needed for vaulting exercises; however, it must not be frightening to

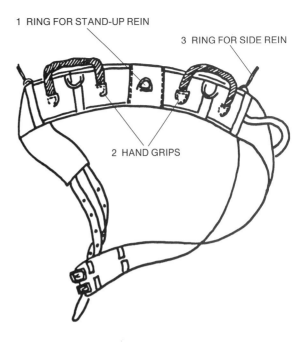

1 RING FOR STAND-UP REIN

3 RING FOR SIDE REIN

2 HAND GRIPS

25 *A vaulting surcingle*

the pony. A **vaulting surcingle** with a correctly fitting pad is needed (**25**). It must be equipped with two hand grips and may have a foot loop. Side reins should be attached to D-rings and used as required. The pony wears a snaffle bridle. Lungeing equipment is needed for the training of the pony.

Helpers must always be on hand whilst a vaulting session is in progress. All the safety rules which apply to riding must also be enforced with this activity.

5 SAFETY AND MEDICAL MANAGEMENT

Safety and Medical Management

Safety is the biggest single concern of the riding lesson, especially in the United States, where lawsuits for every imaginable cause have become the norm. In situations where there are disabled individuals involved with horses, the entire teaching team must constantly focus on safety issues.

There are several safety measures which groups can implement in order to help avoid accident or injury. The first is to devise a plan in case of an emergency. This plan, once written, can be practised at intervals to make sure that all members of the RDA team are able to carry it out. This plan could include what to do if an emergency occurs in the riding arena, as well as what to do in case of fire or other non-arena related incidents.

In relation to the **safety plan**, it is also a good idea to have safety information posted beside the centre's telephone. Such information should include exact directions on how to reach the facility plus relevant telephone numbers, so that the caller – who may be flustered at the time – can give specific instructions to the emergency services.

A second area for safety consideration would be having **a first aid kit** supplied with all the major necessary items in an accessible place. A horse first aid kit is also a must for RDA groups. The Red Cross and the local veterinarian can give advice on what these kits should contain and will also give instruction on their use.

In addition, every riding centre should devise its own facility **safety check**, which would include scrutinizing every corner of the facility on a regular basis, and would be conducted by a safety assessment team. This operates under the theory that several pairs of eyes are better than one. In this way, potential problems are caught before they become hazards.

Every RDA instructor should have basic first aid training. All RDA riding instructors should hold a first aid certificate in Great Britain and under the new instructor certification programme being implemented by NARHA, this type of training will be required for all those seeking therapeutic instructor status.

Another major area for consideration in the riding lesson is that of medical management. Many instructors, although well intentioned about wishing to help disabled individuals learn to ride, have little or no understanding of disabilities. They are, therefore, unable to judge whether a specific riding activity might indeed be harmful to an individual rider with a certain type of problem. The first rule for every RDA instructor should be 'Do No Harm.' So it is important for all riding instructors to work closely with the medical profession to assess each disabled rider for fitness not only to ride, but also to participate in the specific activities associated with each component of riding.

Assisting and handling disabled riders

Helpers require little medical knowledge to be of benefit to the group. As long as they are aware of each of their riders' needs and abilities, they can assist them efficiently if and when necessary. It does help, however, if in the course of their association with the group they learn the definitions of disabilities. The group physiotherapist should be available to hold regular briefing sessions, explaining to helpers in general terms the problems that may be encountered with each individual disability.

An attentive helper, who gets to know his riders well, anticipating their responses to different situations, will, by his knowledge of each individual, be instrumental in spotting signs of fatigue or discomfort. These signs are not always apparent to the instructor, therefore any information passed from the helper to the instructor regarding each individual rider will be welcomed.

Different approaches are needed for riders who have physical handicaps and riders who have mental handicaps; however, this should not be over-emphasized. Once again, advice should be obtained from the group physiotherapist about how to treat the physically handicapped and the special education teacher about the mentally handicapped.

Instructors, therapists and helpers will find it helpful, to gain a better insight into the rider's background, if they make a visit to the rider's hospital or special school. As long as adequate prior notice is given, most principals and senior nursing officers are agreeable to this.

As well as knowing what to do, helpers are given a great deal of confidence in handling the riders if they are aware of what *not* to do; for example:

1   A joint must never be forced.

2   A rider who is paraplegic or has spina bifida should not be allowed to sit still for more than ten minutes without easing the pressure. This can be done fairly easily with a push or a pull up, or shifting position; or by the use of an over-numnah.

3   When a rider has one 'good side' he should be encouraged to use both sides, not letting him use his good side only. When using his afflicted side he must try harder.

Special equipment for safety, comfort and assistance

It should always be remembered, when thinking of using special equipment for a particular rider, that it should not be used unless it is really necessary or really useful. However, intelligent use of equipment which has been carefully chosen can help many disabled riders and those who teach them. Riding should be kept as enjoyable as possible and the use of special equipment must be to ensure the rider's safety and comfort only. The only piece of equipment that must be used by all disabled riders is a safety helmet, or crash cap, unless their disability prevents this, when alternative headgear must be devised.

Before selecting equipment one must consider that it should not tie the rider to the horse in any way, or restrict or interfere with the rider's balance, movement or contact with the horse. The horse must also be considered and no equipment used should annoy, irritate or cause it discomfort or risk of injury of any sort.

It is very important for the rider to look the same as his fellow riders or at least as little 'different' as possible. Therefore, as well as the equipment being used being comfortable for him, it must not cause him embarrassment either. If a decision has been made, usually between the instructor and physiotherapist, that special equipment is needed, then it must be suited to the individual's needs. The rider's disability, age, physique and temperament are all deciding factors of what might suit that individual, and also the actual amount of riding he does.

Individuals and more experienced riders are often able, by trial and error, to find equipment which, when carefully fitted, can help them achieve the independence they seek. Generally, the simpler the equipment, the more useful it is. Many groups cannot afford to buy expensive special equipment, and many find that they do better with a limited choice of generally useful articles.

There follows a description of some equipment which is regularly used in many groups, and some things which are loaned around the groups, as and when a particular rider needs that piece of equipment. However, it should be noted that there are many other items used, some of which are devised by the groups themselves, for particular cases.

Ankle guards are used by riders whose disability makes their toes drop and the stirrup iron press against the front of the rider's ankle. This is often the case with spastic children. Figure **26** is an example of a specially made ankle guard which was made at the Winford Hospital. However, hockey guards, which can be obtained from sports shops, are an available substitute.

Artificial arms and legs are not usually a problem when riding. Artificial arms can be fitted with a split hoop for use with shortened or ladder reins. Successful riding can take place with riders who have artificial leg/s; however, buckets or sockets may be found useful and can be stitched to the saddle flap, or hung on shortened stirrup leathers to accommodate the stump of an amputed leg (**27a**). A swivel stirrup leather (**27b**) may also be used with benefit to riders with artificial legs with ridged feet.

27a) *Bucket or socket*

1 ARTIFICIAL LEG

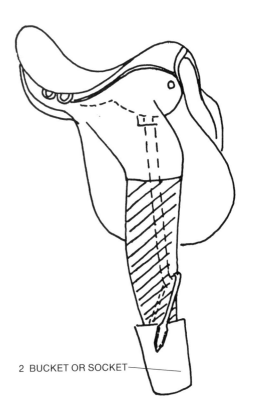

2 BUCKET OR SOCKET

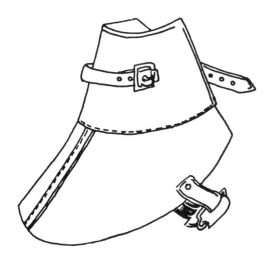

26 *Ankle guard*

27b) *Swivel stirrup leather*

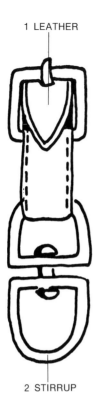

1 LEATHER

2 STIRRUP

A **bar** made of steel which can be shaped into a half-moon, can be built into the fore arch of the saddle and covered with sorbo rubber and leather so that it resembles the pommels of a side saddle. These lie across the upper part of the thighs and provide considerable security when combined with a modern deep-seated saddle.

Blind aids such as bells and bleepers can be used to help the rider with direction.

Boots and shoes which are worn when riding should have an adequate heel and a long sole. To ease the pulling or pushing which might be needed when putting on or taking off both long and short boots and shoes, zips and/or safety buckles which enable the boot to be opened are a great help. Casual shoes, plimsoles and sandals or other footwear without a heel are dangerous for riding and must not be used.

Caps – hard hats – cap keepers. Hard hats are essential and must be worn whatever the activity. The British Standards Institute's Kite Mark ensures that the hard hat meets safety standards, and should be the only choice when purchasing a hat for any rider. Hats are fitted with a safety chin strap, which is secured to the hat at three points. Once a hard hat has suffered a severe blow it must be discarded. Where a group is catering for many different sizes of riders, hats can be padded with cotton wool or sorbo rubber, plastic foam or plasticote and fitted with a separate chinstrap as shown in figure **28** to ensure a snug fit.

28 *Hard hat*

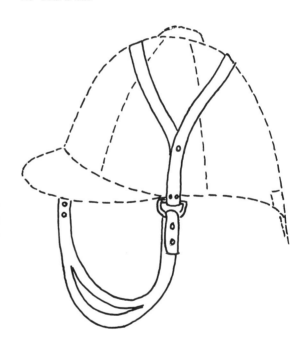

SEPARATE CHIN-STRAP FOR DIFFERENT SIZES OF HAT

Soft inner skull caps can also be worn to enable a hard hat to be worn by different sized heads.

'Emergency only' belts are an essential piece of equipment for every member group. These safety belts are adjustable, so can be used by many different riders. For children between six and twelve the measurement would be about 55 cm (22 inches) from each end of the webbing, with the strap punched with a number of holes. The webbing should be 10 cm (2 inches) wide, more for a larger and heavier rider (**29**). The purpose of the belt is to give the rider a sense of security and the helper something sturdy and uncomplicated to grab hold of should this be necessary. They can be used to help maintain the rider's balance in the saddle if this is necessary, but must be dispensed with once the rider gains sufficient balance.

29 *'Emergency only' belt*

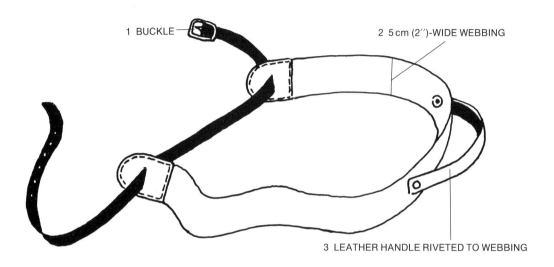

1 BUCKLE

2 5 cm (2'')-WIDE WEBBING

3 LEATHER HANDLE RIVETED TO WEBBING

The pelvic belt technique uses a wide belt (**30**), placed around the rider's pelvis, below the iliac crests. On either side of the belt a strap is attached which is in line with the rider's hip joint. The physiotherapist and a trained side helper holds the straps and provide an equal downward pull. Because the belt is below the rider's centre of gravity, his stability is greatly increased, allowing him to accommodate more effectively to the proprioceptive (movement) input from the horse. This use of the belt can also be modified to provide varying types of therapeutic input by the trained hippotherapist.[2]

Clothing is an important factor to consider when riding. It does not have to be correct riding clothing but must be comfortable. Jodhpurs or trousers are of course essential and trousers often provide protection from rubbing. All clothing

30 *Pelvic belt (Barbara L. Glasgow, P.T., Tobyhanna, PA, USA.)*

should be zipped up or fastened appropriately to ensure it does not interfere with rider, horse or helper.

Handles made from rolled leather are of immense value to beginners or nervous riders, and provide a firmer hold than neck straps. For most riders a handle 30 cm (12 inches) long, with buckles at either end to fasten to the 'D's of the saddle (**31a**), is fine. However, heavier riders, who tend to pull the 'D's off, should use a handle of rolled leather 65 cm (26 inches) long which is attached by loops to the girth straps (**31b**) for extra security. These handles should be used only for as long as necessary as they tend to get the rider 'behind the movement'. The riders should progress to neck straps with handles when ready.

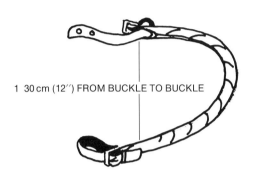

1 30 cm (12″) FROM BUCKLE TO BUCKLE

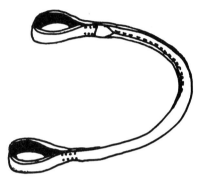

1 65 cm (26″) LONG

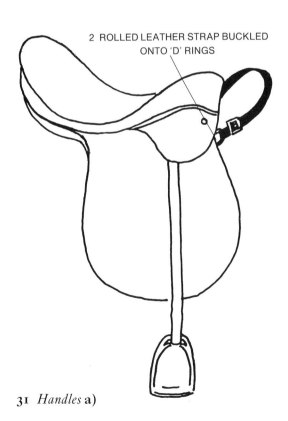

2 ROLLED LEATHER STRAP BUCKLED ONTO 'D' RINGS

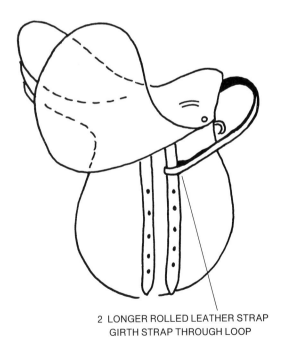

2 LONGER ROLLED LEATHER STRAP GIRTH STRAP THROUGH LOOP

31 *Handles* **a)**   **b)**

Knee grips made of rubber and **knee protectors** of leather, fastened with straps above and below the knees, give protection over trousers and have been found helpful by some riders with weak legs.

Knee rolls give greater security at faster paces and for jumping. They are fitted to most modern saddles and are a real help to riders with weak or artificial legs.

Neck straps are probably the most widely used pieces of equipment throughout member groups. They are very beneficial for many activities, especially for riders who have reached the stage of cantering, jumping and hacking out. The best neck straps are those that consist of a handle attached to the top of a breast plate with correct attachments to the saddle and girth (**32**). Neck straps should always be worn for riding off a lead line.

32 *Neckstrap*

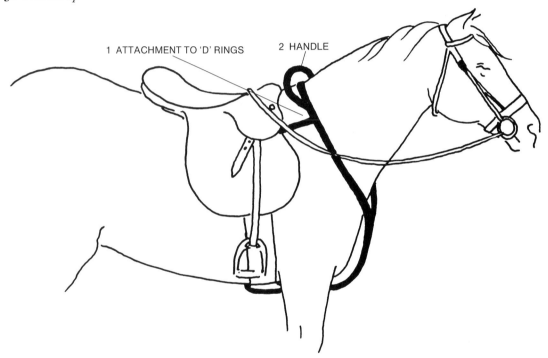

1 ATTACHMENT TO 'D' RINGS   2 HANDLE

Check or grass reins are used to stop the pony putting his head down to eat, or to stop a pony from snatching the reins out of the rider's hands. These should be made with strong leather with a snap hook at each end. One end is fastened to the 'D' of the saddle, while the leather strap is passed through the brow band loop and is then clipped onto the bit (**33**). The strap must be long enough to allow the horse to move and relax his head normally. Temporary grass reins can be made from binder twine and fixed in the same way.

Ladder reins are very useful to riders who have artificial or severely disabled arm/s. Figure **34a** shows how three pieces of leather are joined to the two reins so that they can be easily shortened and lengthened.

Non-slip reins (**34b**) can be plaited leather, laced or rubber-covered. Webbing and plaited cotton 'Dartnall' reins are used as alternatives.

33 *Check or grass reins*

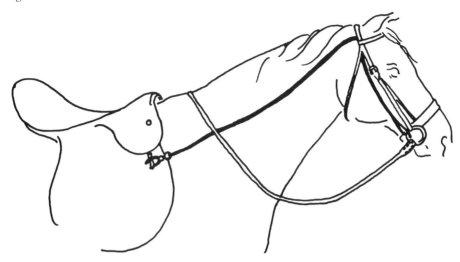

The reins chosen should be suited to the size of the rider's hands. They should not be hard or abrasive when dry nor slippery when wet, as nylon plaited reins tend to be.

Looped reins are also useful providing an alternative to the ladder rein (**34c**).

Dowled reins are another alternative to ladder reins and are useful for riders who have difficulty with grasp. The wooden dowels should be spaced 10 centimetres (4 inches) apart (**34d**).

34 *Reins*

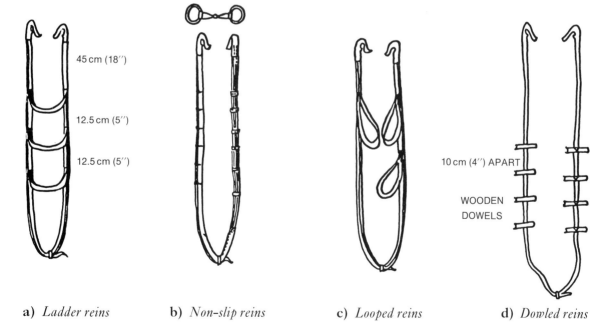

45 cm (18″)

12.5 cm (5″)

12.5 cm (5″)

10 cm (4″) APART

WOODEN
DOWELS

a) *Ladder reins*   **b)** *Non-slip reins*   **c)** *Looped reins*   **d)** *Dowled reins*

Shortened reins are often easier to manage and avoid the possibility of the spare length being caught up in some way. While the normal length of a rein is about 1.5 m (five feet), these can often be reduced by about 30 cm (1 ft) or more according to the size of the pony.

Clip-on reins, such as cheap clip-on webbing reins, are easy and quick to attach to the headcollar.

Back rest. A canvas numnah to be worn over the saddle with a padded back support that can be brought into contact with the rider and give extra support has been used.

Foot rest. This can be made of wood and screwed firmly to the stirrup iron to provide a sole on which the foot can rest more easily than the iron alone.

Rubber bands can be put around the heel or toe to secure the foot to the iron; they are easily breakable in case of a fall so safety is not affected.

Saddles. *Different types* of saddles, such as Australian stock saddles, modern central position saddles, side saddles and Western saddles have been used successfully by a number of disabled riders for a number of various reasons. The modern central position saddle should be used

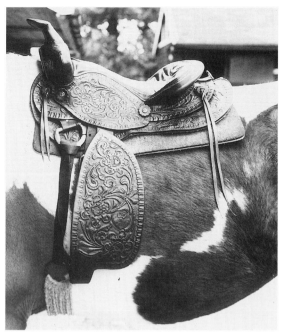

b) *A Western saddle*

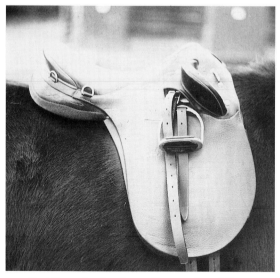

35 *Saddles* **a)** *An Australian stock saddle*

wherever possible. The Pony Club approved saddle made to a master pattern and marked on the stirrup bar is a sound choice for children. The Australian stock saddle (**35a**), with its specially designed pommel, gives great security and is valuable for riding holidays and outdoor riding. The Western saddle (**35b**) with its high pommel and deep seat provides comfort and security and assists in developing good balance. It is useful for pony trekking as well. Side saddles have been successfuly used by both women and men and seem most appropriate for those with right-leg-below-the-knee amputations. Long distance saddles are generally used for Spina Bifida. For other riders, stirrups may be attached (**35c**).

Basket saddles are dangerous and should not be used as they strap the rider to the horse. On rare occasions when a limbless thalidomide child who could not ride otherwise is to ride, they can ride in a basket saddle, but must never be strapped in. Helpers must provide the necessary support.

c) *A long distance saddle (35a, b and c pony Riding for the Disabled Trust)*

Saddles with built-in leg rests (36) may be made for the special needs of the rider with severe leg disability.

Saddle numnah or felt can be used to advantage by many severely handicapped children. Those with a tree forepart or steel arch are preferable to treeless models because they are less easily displaced. A model fitted with a steel and leather covered handle 7.5 cm (3 inches) high and 12.5 cm ($5\frac{1}{2}$ inches) wide fitted to the tree forepart has proved very useful in giving a sense of security to severely handicapped and anxious small children.

Sheepskin strapped over the saddle provides great comfort as an alternative to foam and/or a felt numnah saddle. A surcingle must always be used to prevent slipping.

Stirrup irons, Devonshire boot. This has a leather-covered toecap to prevent the toe from dropping down and through the stirrup (37). It must always be used if the rider does not wear shoes with adequate heels. Keepers that help secure the stirrup leather in place can be attached to the saddle flap. These are useful where a rider has difficulty in keeping his feet in the iron.

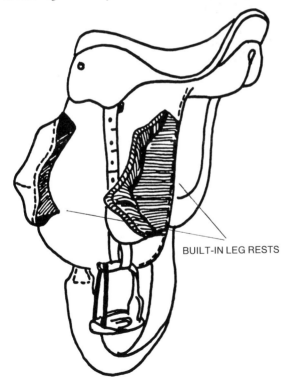

BUILT-IN LEG RESTS

36 *Saddle with built-in leg rests*

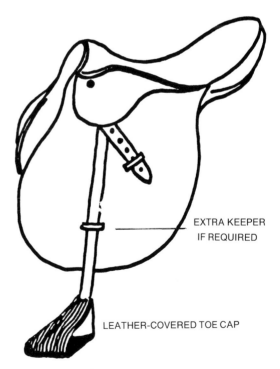

EXTRA KEEPER
IF REQUIRED

LEATHER-COVERED TOE CAP

37 *Devonshire boot*

Kornakoof stirrup irons have the eye of the iron set to one side.

Toe-raising rubber (38) is made of a piece of motor-cycle inner tubing with a bottling jar ring and fastened to the iron and under the toe. It has been used with good effect where the muscle is flaccid, but should not be used with spastic children.

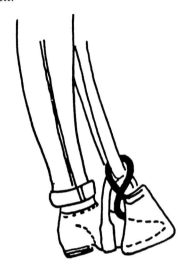

38 *Toe raising rubber*

Peacock safety stirrup irons are nearly always used for riders with disabilities as an extra precaution. The outside of the iron has a rolled rubber belt attached to the top and bottom of the

39 *Peacock safety stirrup*

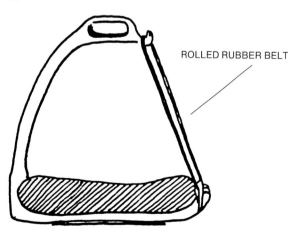

ROLLED RUBBER BELT

stirrup (39). In case of a fall this would pull off and release the rider's foot immediately.

Comfort, assistance and riding position

Where medical management is applied to the actual act of riding, it seems more appropriate for profoundly handicapped people, those who may not have been considered suitable for riding within RDA groups in Great Britain, to have hippotherapy. These individuals may not be considered suitable to take to RDA groups because:

1   Their large wheelchairs take up too much precious room in the transport available.

2   These riders can only tolerate a short time on the horse, probably a maximum of 10 minutes.

3   These riders are likely to have little or no head control and no sitting balance.

4   The riders' participation in the actual ride may not be obvious at first glance. They have to be taken as individuals, not in a group ride.

It would be foolish to imagine that one can put a profoundly handicapped child on a horse without specific knowledge of his disability. In such a case the physiotherapist and the instructor work together to achieve the most comfortable position for each rider.

In the initial stages, it does not seem important how the rider is positioned on the horse. Sometimes the rider starts by lying across the horse like a dead cowboy. The rider can be balanced quite accurately over the horse's back and the warmth and movement help to relax contractions in the arms and legs.

Whenever possible (although not necessarily for hippotherapy or developmental riding therapy), the instructor and physiotherapist try to get the rider sitting on the horse in a normal position. The horse is an invaluable aid to those who have problems of balance. It is surprisingly difficult to balance while immobile in a wheelchair. The rhythmic movement of the horse enables the rider's muscles to make small complementary movements and sitting unsupported often becomes an achievable goal for those who cannot sit upright in a chair.

The upper part of the body is interfered with as little as possible. Provided that the knee or ankle is held in the correct position, it is virtually impossible for the rider to fall, even if he loses his balance; and he can adjust his position at will.

With the smaller rider, the helpers can rest an elbow on the pony's withers, in the attitude of someone about to embark on a bout of arm wrestling (**40a**) and hold the rider's hand in an elevated position in front of them. With legs in position and the hands held up, most riders can achieve a degree of balance and head control. The hand support can be adjusted and provides a more interactive support than can be gained by leaning on the arch of a roller. It is, however, most uncomfortable for the helpers who will need to change sides frequently.

40 *Different holds:* **a) b) c) d)** *(Francis Thomas-Davies)*

gradually relax and the head is lifted; minimal support should be given. The side helper's outside hand can hold the ankle, with the inside forearm resting across the rider's thigh and the fingers used to reinforce the hand grip on the neckstrap (**40b**). This can frequently be reduced to holding the ankle with the inside hand (**40c**).

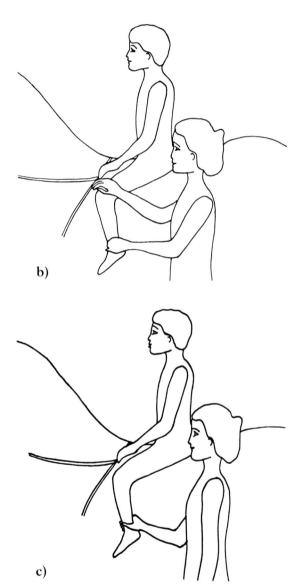

b)

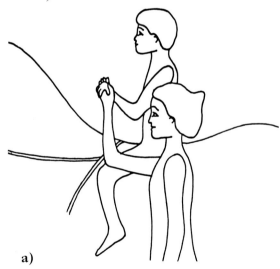

a)

Whenever possible, the rider should sit astride, holding on to the neck strap with head and hands in mid-line. When the horse walks forward it is often surprising, with the encouragement of the helpers, how the rider manages to improve his position. The legs

c)

The helper can feel the position of the rider and is aware if the balance is suddenly lost. With a helper on either side, even if the rider flops he cannot fall off.

If the rider has very tight adductors, the helper's inside forearm can be placed on the horse under the rider's thigh (**40d**) this slightly lifts the leg and takes the weight off the hips.

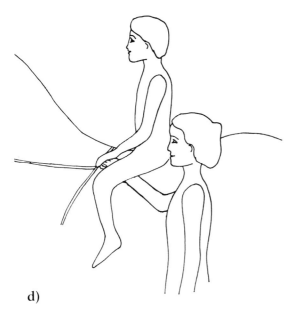

d)

With careful consideration for the needs of the individual rider, the position, speed and direction of the movement can be varied in order to get the maximum benefit from the session. This however should not detract from the enjoyment of the ride. Hippotherapy provides an invaluable extension to physiotherapy carried out in the open air and with the horse as the main therapist.[2]

Placing riders

Riders should not be put into groups which will not suit them. It is never a good idea to mix mentally and physically handicapped riders in one group. This does seem to have a negative effect on physically handicapped riders and lowers their enthusiasm.

Where possible, riders with the same type of disability should be put into one group. This allows the instructor to plan a lesson that will benefit all the riders and allows them to learn to ride on equal terms with each other.

Adults and children should also ride separately. If it becomes necessary for them to be mixed for any one session, due to unavoidable circumstances, then that is what it should be: one session. Arrangements must be made for further sessions to be separated.

If groups find that they have a range of riders, but cannot cope with the amount of sessions needed to accommodate them all, then the group should either think about expanding or about placing riders in other groups. Four to six riders in one lesson is ideal, any more and the lesson may become out of control. Of course when there are facilities for individuals to ride in smaller classes or even individually, then they will benefit greatly from the instructor's undivided attention.

Larger groups, which already cater for a wide range of riders, will have the added opportunity to place riders into groups according to ability: those that are total beginners, those that have some ability and those that are good riders, etc. A rider who is in the right group will progress far quicker than if he were put into an incorrect group for his individual needs.

Rider awareness of safety procedures

Most handicapped riders are able to understand that riding can be dangerous if safety procedures are not followed. There are many ways in which the group can make riders aware of the safety aspects of riding.

Firstly, the instructor can give a talk about safety procedures before each new student is allowed to ride. At the start of each new riding session and at intervals thereafter, the instructor might read out the safety code and procedures for accidents for the benefit of the riders. The helpers can help the riders to understand what is being said, giving demonstrations if necessary. There should always be details of what to do in an accident and any safety code the group imposes should be pinned up, where everyone can see it. It must also be clearly readable.

If there is a lecture room or a warm place where the waiting riders can gather before or after their lesson, then spare helpers or parents can conduct theory lessons. As explained in Chapter 6, it is of great help if riders can use a workbook. Safety can be conveyed in a theory lesson and what the riders write and draw in their workbook can show how much they understand the safety procedures.

Discussions on everyday things, bringing in the safety aspect, can be most helpful. For example, in a discussion of tacking up, whoever is talking might go on to explain that it is important to keep the tack oiled and supple and what will happen if the tack is not kept in good repair. If it is raining and the riders cannot ride, then instead of packing up and going home, they would benefit greatly from theory sessions. Nearly every rider will learn something from theory lessons and the more they are given the opportunity to be involved in such lessons the more they will learn and understand, benefiting them both on and off the horse.

6 THE LESSON

Confidence for all

When trying to establish confidence in disabled riders, which is essential before they can learn to ride, the instructor and helpers first need to establish a level of communication which suits each particular individual. Students with mental handicaps need to be treated carefully. It is imperative that there is somebody familiar to them on hand at all times.

Some of the communication problems that commonly occur are:

a) Difficulties in understanding words (vocabulary), sentences (syntax) and long sentences (length of utterance).

b) Unintelligible speech.

c) Poor attention, easily distracted by the things going on around them.

d) Poor sequencing abilities.

e) Poor memory, especially auditory memory.

f) Poor discrimination. That is to say, they may not see or hear the small differences, e.g. 'wash' and 'watch' sound the same.

There are ways in which instructors, special education teachers and trained helpers can help towards effective communication with riders who have mental handicaps and so build up their confidence in riding. Firstly, the instructor, special education teacher and helpers should remember never to shout as shouting only serves to confuse and upset riders.

a) All messages should be spoken clearly and slowly, in simple sentences.

b) All speech should be accompanied with gestures or can be accompanied by sign language (Makaton) if known.

c) Any vocabulary to be used should be chosen carefully and stuck to; if something is called big one moment it should not then be referred to as large the next.

d) The number of words in a sentence should be simplified to the essential ones carrying the meaning.

e) In a one-to-one situation it is important that the instructor gains the rider's attention before he starts to speak. This can be achieved by saying the rider's name or touching him prior to speaking.

f) Face-to-face communication should be sought whenever possible. This enables the rider to get maximum clues from the instructor's facial expression and for the instructor to see if the rider has attended and understood what has been said.

New skills will need to be done many times before they are really learned. This is called *overlearning* and is essential if skills are to be retained. If errors occur, they should be corrected in a positive way with a practical demonstration where possible. To avoid confusion, economy of words is paramount.

Some learners need a lot of time and cannot deal with more than one or at most two facts at a time. If sequencing problems are present, then tasks will need to be broken down into stages in the learning phase. Instructors should teach 'little and often' bearing in mind the individual attention span. Generally the mentally handicapped have difficulty in understanding the following:

a) Negatives: 'Don't throw that hoop' may be heard as 'Throw that hoop'.

b) Prepositions: behind, in front, beside, etc. are often not understood.

c) Comparatives and superlatives, e.g. the forms big, bigger, biggest are often confusing.

d) Time: the concept of time is generally poorly developed. These students live in the here and now, and require immediate gratification.

e) Number concepts are often poorly developed. These students can often count by rote but have no sense of number values.

f) Mentally handicapped riders have a very literal understanding of language.

Once communication has been established with the rider who has a mental disability, it is then easier to interpret what he is trying to say or do and to know how he will react in certain situations.

Creating the right atmosphere

Every rider must enjoy his riding sessions if he is to derive the maximum benefit. Before any riding lessons take place, the rider's whole attitude towards the idea of riding should be considered.

41 *Many riders progress to independent riding through self-determination and a wish to improve themselves. (Don Corcoran)*

What is his normal character? How does he react to new things? How is he likely to behave, whilst riding or otherwise? A **discussion** with those who know him well, such as his parents or teacher, will give an overall picture.

Before the lesson is to begin, the student, as he is now known, should be allowed a period of time to relax and mentally prepare for the task in hand. A light discussion with the instructor and helpers, even a few **jokes**, will help to make the rider feel comfortable in this new environment. A relaxed atmosphere should then continue throughout the lesson. The instructor, in the lesson environment, is very important to the students. The instructor's word is law. Many riders with disabilities have been heard to say, 'It is right, because *my* instructor said so!' The influence of the instructor on the students is tremendous. This has to be so if he is going to be able to control the class safely.

The first aim of the instructor, using his helpers to convey certain messages, is to make the students really *feel* that riding is fun; something they can do, with aims and goals they themselves can achieve. The students will soon want to please the instructor, with the attitude 'Look at me, look what I can do.' **(41)** Once the students want to please, they soon develop a determination to want to improve themselves.

Discipline must not be forgotten. But there can be discipline within a happy overall tone. The student will soon realize that riding is a serious yet happy business.

Mounting

It is often thought that the riding lesson begins once the students are mounted and assembled. In fact, however, the riding lesson may begin as the students arrive at the riding centre. Certainly, mounting is an important part of the process, as is dismounting. For the rider with a handicap this process can be very time-consuming and very complex.

There are many factors which contribute to the success of mounting the handicapped rider, and which affect the value of the task. Initially, before evaluating each rider for the most appropriate type of mount, the following preparations should be made:

a) The horse must be trained to accept the different types of mounting procedures that will be used.

b) The riding instructor needs to be familiar with all of the possibilities for mounting, and must have practised these successfully on 'mock' students before attempting such procedures on the handicapped student.

c) The necessary equipment must be in place; for example, a safe, well-constructed mounting ramp **(42)**, and/or a mounting block **(43)**, placed in an area which is distraction free.

d) Helpers who will be assisting with the mounting process also need to be properly trained in advance.

e) Most important, the rider needs pre-mounting instruction to ready him for mounting. In some cases, this need be only verbal instruction, but often riders with handicaps benefit from also seeing what will take place.

So, a demonstration mounting may help the student. It is important, as well, to ask the rider for his views. Many riders understand their disabilities and bodies, and have a good sense of what they can do and how best to accomplish it.

The mounting procedure for each student will depend largely on what handicap the rider has. In addition, the height and weight of the rider, muscle strength, co-ordination, and body awareness should be analysed. Another determining factor will be if the rider is wheelchair-bound, uses crutches or canes, leg braces, or wears other assistive or prescriptive devices. It is important to have a physiotherapist's advice in designing the proper mounting procedure for each rider, particularly for those who are physically handicapped.

The psychological state of each rider should

42 *A safe, sturdy, portable mounting ramp.*
(Elizabeth Beckerlegge)

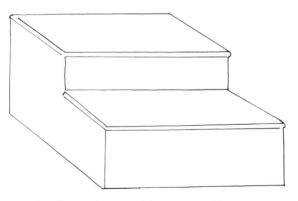

43 *A safe, sturdy, portable mounting block*

also be assessed to determine the best mounting procedure. Many riders, particularly beginners, are apprehensive about mounting. Their nervousness causes body tension and muscle stiff-

ness and tightness. A sympathetically designed mounting process can greatly relieve the anxious rider, and eliminate some of the physical symptoms that impede successful mounting.

Before the mounting begins the pony should be brought into position at the ramp or mounting block. The leader must stand in front of the pony's head, and the instructor and trained helpers must be in position. Where a mounting ramp is used for riders who use a wheelchair the wheelchair should be secured into position before the mounting procedure begins. Mounting may take place from either the near (left) side of the pony or the off (right) side, depending on which arm- and foot-rest have been removed from the wheelchair.

There are eight basic procedures in mounting:[1]

1 Total lift – The rider is lifted completely into position on the horse by a trained person (a hoist is sometimes used for heavy riders). Where a rider has been mounted using a mounting ramp the horse should be walked forward until the stirrups are clear of the ramp before the rider's feet are put into the stirrups.

2 Assistive lift from wheelchair – The rider is positioned on a mounting ramp with the wheelchair facing the pony's head, the instructor, facing the rider, puts his arms securely around the rider's back and with his knees against the rider's, lifts the rider forward, swivels the rider around and lowers him on to the centre of the saddle in a side-sit position. The trained helper on the opposite side of the pony assists the rider in putting his right leg over the front of the saddle

and in obtaining an astride position with the instructor supporting the left leg and rider's back and the trained helper supporting the right. With the rider in this position the pony is carefully moved forward and once the stirrups are clear of the ramp the rider's legs are lowered and placed into the stirrups (**44a, b, c and d**)

3 Partial assistive wheelchair transfer – Here the rider is working towards more independent mounting. The wheelchair is placed on the ramp, again facing the pony's head, but it is put as near to the saddle as possible. The rider

44 *Assistive lift from wheelchair*
a) *Horse in place*

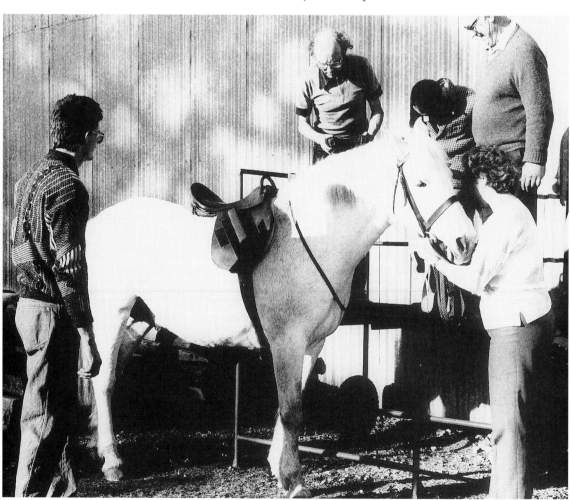

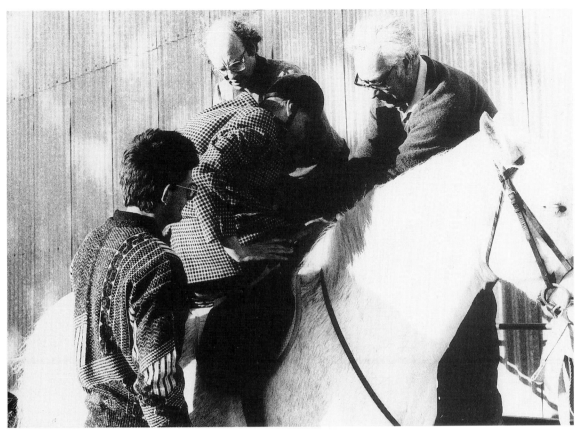

b) *Rider in side-sit position*

then manoeuvres himself into a side-sit position on the saddle, with the instructor supporting the rider's back. The same procedure as with the assistive lift then follows, with the rider trying to adjust to a normal astride position with as little assistance as possible.

4 Wheelchair transfer with minimum assistance – Here the rider is wheeled up the ramp and the wheelchair is placed into position. When the arm and foot rests have been removed the rider mounts to an astride position himself, with the trained helper standing by. Usually the rider will lift his right leg over the saddle and slide into an astride position in one motion. His legs should still be supported until the stirrups are clear of the ramp.

5 Crutch/walker mount from ramp – Once the instructor has helped the rider up the ramp

and they are standing in the correct position for mounting (this may be on either side of the pony) the instructor then holds the rider securely with his left arm around the rider's chest; the instructor then removes the crutch with his right hand. The rider puts his free hand on to the saddle. The instructor switches his arms and places his right arm around the rider's chest, then the rider gives the other crutch to a side helper. The rider is then encouraged to mount normally with the reins in the left hand and the left foot in the stirrup. The instructor supports the rider while he puts his right leg over the back of the pony. The instructor and trained helper assist the rider in adjusting to a comfortable position. A rider with crutches who may not be able to mount in this way, can, with the assistance of the instructor, first establish a side-sit position and then put the right leg over the front of the saddle to sit astride.

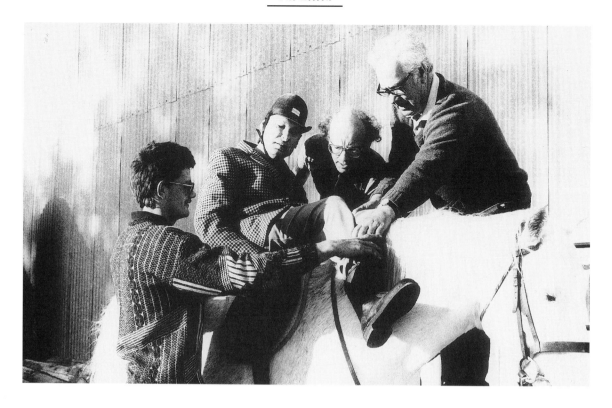

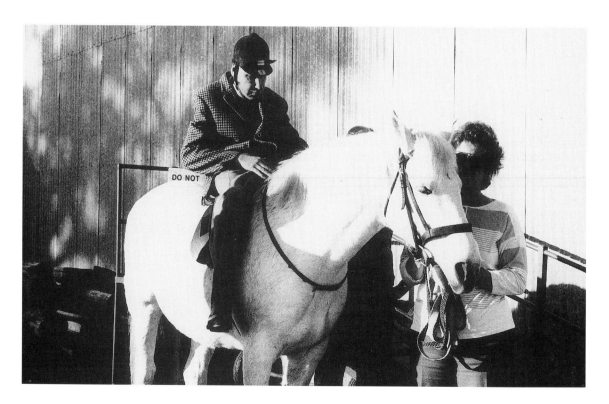

c) *(top left) Rider being assisted in putting his right leg over the horse's neck*

d) *(bottom left) Horse is moved forward and rider's feet are put into stirrups (44a, b, c and d Elizabeth Beckerlegge)*

6 Normal mount – partial assistance – Here the rider may mount from a ramp or a mounting block. The instructor helps the rider to place his foot into the stirrup, then supports the rider while he lifts his leg over the back of the pony. The trained helper on the opposite side then assists the rider and instructor in establishing a comfortable astride position (**45a, b and c**).

7 Normal mount – minimum assistance – This mount is fairly similar to the partial assistance mount in that the rider puts his foot into the stirrup and puts the other leg over the back of the pony, however, only minimum assistance is given and the rider is encouraged towards more independence.

8 Normal Mount – A normal mount is where a rider faces the pony's quarters, places his foot into the stirrup, propels himself upwards putting his other leg over the back of the saddle and sits correctly astride. Many individuals with a handicap are able to mount in this way, without assistance, once they are confident.

When students are at ease with the mounting

45 *Normal mount partial assistance*
45a) *Rider places foot in stirrup, then . . .*

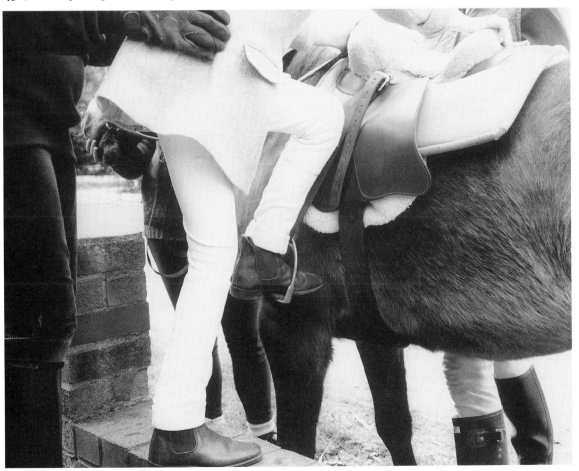

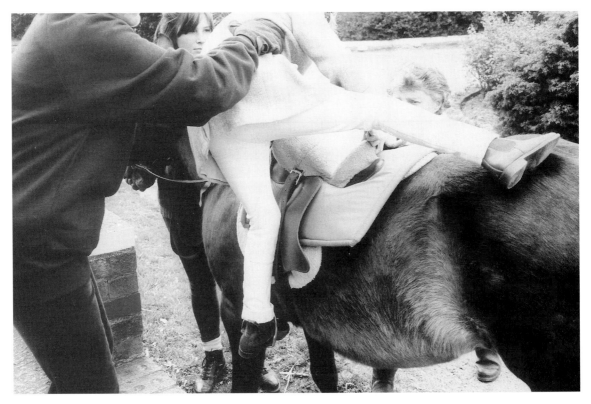

45b) *is assisted in putting her leg over the pony's back and . . .*

procedure, they should be encouraged to mount normally, using a mounting block, as long as this can do no harm in any way and they are physically capable of doing so. Mounting should not take place from the ground, as this puts a strain on the pony's back. If a purpose-built mounting block is not available a safe alternative should be used.

The lesson

Once all of the disabled riders in a class are mounted, the class can begin.

During **warm-up**, the rider has the opportunity to 'switch gears', putting aside other worries and concerns, and becoming focused on the horse and the riding activities. Here too the rider has a chance to warm and relax muscles that might be stiff or tense.

After a very few minutes of warm up, the riders will be ready for some **exercises**. These should be designed with the whole body in mind, and should complement the skill lesson being taught that day. For example, if right and left turns will be taught during riding skills, then exercises emphasizing right/left discrimination would be appropriate. Exercises should be challenging to the rider, and emphasize **co-ordination**, **balance** and **postural control**. This is an ideal place for the physiotherapist to be involved. He can advise the instructor on the best exercises for each rider, showing the instructor how each exercise should be demonstrated and performed. He can also advise on the kinds of handling techniques helpers should use to ease each rider's performance of a given exercise.

The major part of the lesson, and the part which will occupy the most time, is the riding skills section. For adapted sport riding this is the crucial part of the riding session. Each rider must be able to understand what is being taught and must be able, with proper adaptation and/or compensation, to perform the required skills. The instructor will find many challenges here, as each rider will require individual attention to his specific needs and requirements.

After the skill has been explained, demon-strated and practised by all the riders in the group, then it is time to have a little fun and relaxation in the form of a **game**, or in the case of Western style riders, a pattern. The game will be best conducted when it reflects the skill the riders have just learned. For example, if the riders have just learned to halt and walk on, then the appropriate game might be 'red light, green light', which would reinforce the skills needed for walking on and halting.

It is important here to advise helpers who are involved with the students not to become too involved in the game and forget that it is the rider and not the helper who is performing the task and

45c) *side helper assists in establishing a correct astride position with feet in stirrups.*

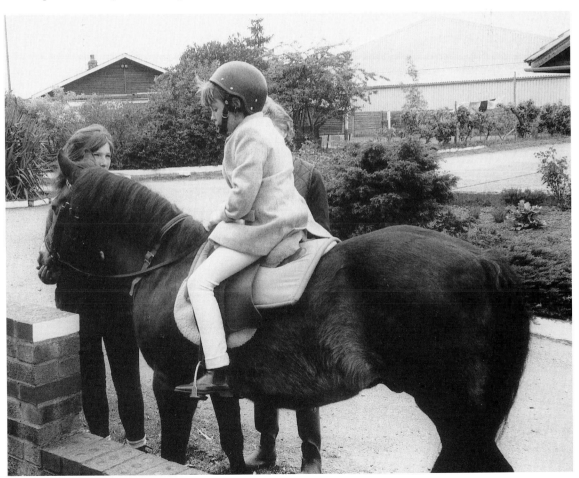

winning the game. Sometimes helpers are so enthusiastic about their rider's success that they over-help the rider and block that rider's chance for self-development.

Then comes the **cool-down**. This is a nice, quiet period of the lesson. It gives each rider a chance to hug and make much of his pony, and enjoy the atmosphere of riding and the environment.

46 *Dismounting to the ground*
a) *Rider takes both feet out of the stirrups, leans forward, . . .*

Dismounting

Dismounting should be undertaken with the same care and attention as mounting. Although many riders may need a ramp to mount, they may be able to dismount to the ground. Again, a physiotherapist can be very useful to the group, giving advice about what method would be best, and how to accomplish the task, keeping in mind the dignity and overall comfort of the rider (**46 a, b, c and d**).

No riding session should take place without the instructor having a **lesson plan**. This is devised in the light of the elements mentioned and the disabilities of the riders included in the lesson. It is important to set long- and short-term goals for each rider at the start of the term. The

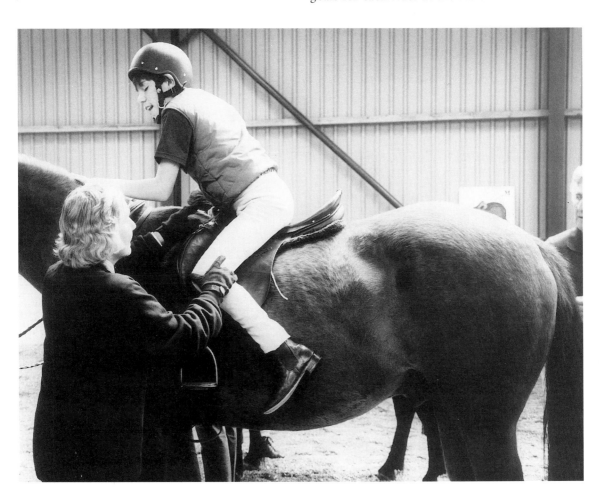

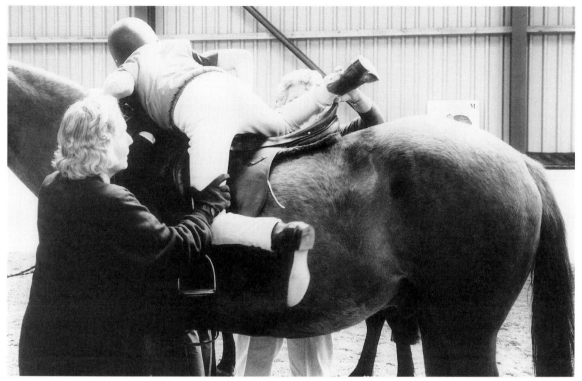

b) *then swings right leg over the back of the saddle,*

c) *lowers himself to the ground, and . . .*

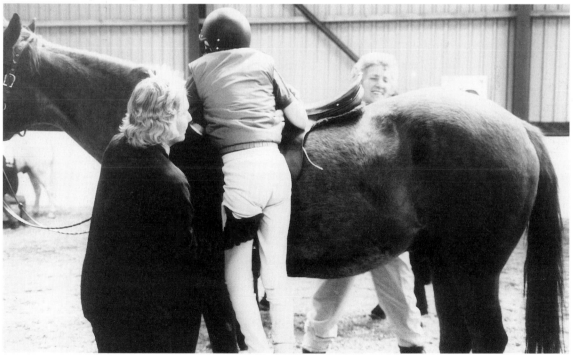

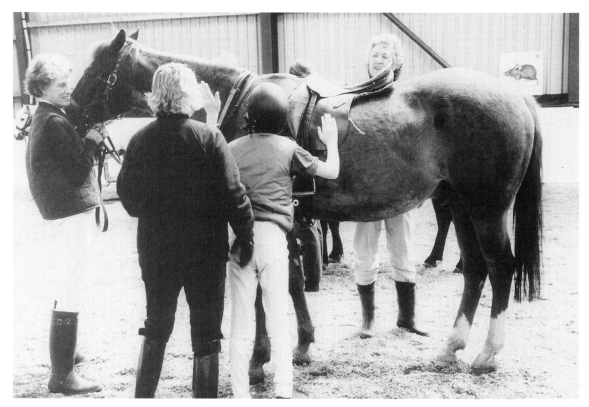

46d) *instinctively gives his horse a pat to say 'thank you'.*

short-term goals will be the building blocks to the accomplishment of a long-term goal; these can be accomplished on a weekly basis. At the end of ten to twelve weeks of performing sequential short-term goals, the long-term goal will have been realized. If the instructor does not know how to design such a riding plan, advice should be sought from other experienced instructors, special education teachers, or from the local school system, where a teacher can help with such a scheme.

The structure of a lesson

As there must be a lesson plan, there must also be a lesson structure. The lesson structure is the format for the lesson, whereas the lesson plan is the ingredients which will fit the format. The best structured lesson is the one that follows all safety procedures and is fun for riders and helpers. To this end the RDA have designed a recommended structure, which instructors should follow and bear in mind when making a lesson plan.

In the United States, seven sections in the riding lesson have been identified: the mount, the warm-up, the exercises, the skill lesson, the game pattern, the cool-down and the dismount.

In the UK, the RDA has identified the different sections which make up the riding lesson as:

Preparation:

1 Instructors should have the lesson planned,

with props ready and/or set out in the school (**47**).

2 Helpers should have the ponies ready, in a straight line.

3 Organizers (see chapter 9) should have equipment ready and riders' records available for consultation.

Briefing:

1 Whilst helpers fit riding hats, check footwear and clothing etc.,

2 The physiotherapist/teacher/escort, briefs the instructor on any problems with the riders.

3 The instructor then issues preliminary briefing to helpers, checks ponies and tack, etc.

Mounting:

Suggested sequence for maximum safety. Note, mounting can be one of the most dangerous aspects of the ride. (If possible, an experienced trained helper or another knowledgeable instructor supervises matching of ponies and mounting, leaving the class instructor free to direct each rider to *open order* riding as soon as mounted and ready.)

1 The side helper then collects the rider, walks/wheels him to mounting block, ramp, etc. Gets rider ready on the block *before*,

2 The leader brings the pony, halts in position and stands in front of the pony.

3 The person supervising mounting (or other) must be ready on the off-side.

4 The leader moves off with side helper, back into line to adjust stirrups, etc. This speeds up the mounting process and is safer.

5 The next rider is then brought immediately to the mounting block, and so on.

47 *A school set up, with bending and trotting poles, ready for the lesson to begin.*

Open order:

Advanced classes ride on the same rein and include school movements. The less able riders may use props, etc. and include stable management. Ride proceeds on either rein, observing the rule of left to left when passing.

1 The class instructor, with the physiotherapist if possible, receives each rider as soon as ready, briefs helpers on one-to-one instruction, then directs each individually to open order riding and/or exercise relevant to disability.

2 Riders who are on a loose lead line concentrate on 'doing their own thing' at their own level, under the guidance of their trained, informed helper.

Demonstration:

This will be given by an able-bodied rider when possible. A class lesson will commence:

1 When all riders are mounted and moving round the school, they then gather into a ride.

2 The instructor asks each rider/helper team if they achieved their goal set for the open order.

3 The instructor announces the theme of the lesson and if possible, demonstrates.

4 The lesson is then given, following as near as possible the BHS format (see Bibliography). The inclusion of various changes of rein are included to improve the balance of riders and ponies.

Activity or game to reinforce lesson:

1 The ride moves into the planned reinforcement of the lesson and previous lessons by use of props or relevant games. Beware of irrelevant games or races or activity which does not exercise the riders.

2 The helpers must not help too much nor over-react to the race.

3 Riders should be extended to their maximum personal capability, ending the lesson on a positive, successful note.

Sum up and dismount:

1 The ride lines up in a straight line rewarding the ponies and giving thanks to helpers.

2 Dismounting should be done correctly as the occasion and/or disability allows.

Debrief, modify and record progress:

1 De-briefing of helpers, therapists, etc.

2 Note-taking for the recording of progress and points to be taken into consideration for the next lesson, etc., follows.

In RDA groups, helpers and instructors are required to fill out an observation card on completion of each lesson for each rider (48). This information, once recorded, will help to show how each rider is progressing and will show in what area a rider needs to develop.

Lead line and lunge lessons

Most riders with disabilities will ride on a lead line. Only those who have progressed sufficiently in the instructor's opinion, or those who have shown themselves to be competent riders, will be allowed to ride off the lead line.

There is a correct way of leading a rider off the lead line:

The leader should walk alongside the pony about level with his shoulder. This helps to keep him in a proper frame which is more beneficial for everyone. The leading rein should be held in the right hand about 15–30 cm (6–12 inches) from the clip. This allows free motion of his head, which is more therapeutic to the rider and less irritating to the horse. The tail end of the lead should be looped in a figure of eight in the left hand to avoid the helper or the horse tripping on it. It should never be coiled around the hand. Proper attire keeps the leader more comfortable and better able to perform his duties.

The leading rein is not there, however, to enable the leader to take the place of the rider. The pony must move forward in walk because of

RIDER OBSERVATION EVALUATION FORM

Name of Rider: _____   Horse: _____

Goals for Rider: _____

School: _____   Start Date: _____

Evaluation Key: Ability

1 cannot perform the task
2 can perform the task with much assistance
3 can perform the task with moderate assistance
4 can perform the task with minimum assistance
5 can perform the task unassisted

Evaluation Key: Mood

a willing, self-motivated
b willing, needs encouragement
c somewhat willing, somewhat motivated
d unwilling, unmotivated

The Lesson: Date: _____

1 Putting on hard hat   _____
2 Mounting the horse   _____
3 Performing the exercises   _____
4 Performing the lesson tasks _____
5 Performing the game tasks   _____
6 Dismounting the horse   _____
7 Taking off hard hat   _____
8 Other: _____   _____

Special remarks: _____
_____
_____
_____
_____

_____   _____

Signature of Instructor   Date completed

48 *Rider observation evaluation form (developed by Jean Tebay)*

the aids applied by the rider and similarly for halt or trot. If the rider does need assistance from the leader, then the leader must coax the pony forward without turning round. The leader should not move in front of the pony and pull him forward. The only time a leader should stand in front of the pony is for mounting, dismounting or when the pony is halted in line.

The leading rein should be attached by a coupling as shown in figure **49**. Ponies should be led by a strong headcollar or cavesson noseband, preferably not the bit, although this is acceptable in some circumstances, such as with a very strong pony.

Lunge lessons can be of excellent value to a nervous or new rider. A lunge lesson would be given to individual students, where the instructor can give his undivided attention to the needs of that individual. Many exercises can be performed whilst on the lunge, without the rider having to physically control the pony. The helpers will still be at the rider's side to assist if necessary. Lungeing can also be of benefit when

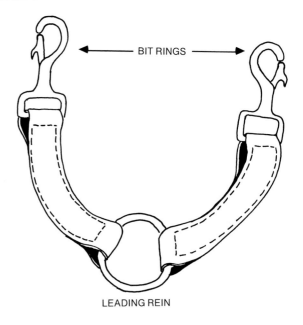

49 *Coupling*

50 *A lunge lesson provides the opportunity of one-to-one instruction.*

teaching a 'theory' lesson or when giving a demonstration with either a disabled or able-bodied rider on top.

When students become more competent and have gained enough confidence, lungeing over poles and caveletti can give riders their first taste of jumping. Again they can concentrate on improving their balance and seat without the worry of having to control the pony or make it jump. Once they have improved in these areas the students then take up the reins and ride the pony, whilst still on the lunge.

Lunge lessons must only be given by an instructor who has a specialist knowledge in this area (50).

51 Bending forward over trotting poles.

Exercises – balance – games

Exercises and games are probably the best way to help the riders progress. However, exercises and games are not the same thing and each have their own benefits. All exercises should be progressive, the value of which is evident in the rider's increased balance and co-ordination. The riders should be encouraged to repeat the exercises more often each time performed, with increasing energy.

The pleasant atmosphere mentioned earlier really is in evidence here, and the ingenuity of the instructor can make a lesson a challenge to improve the rider's performance.

Development of balance is encouraged by exercises. This is very important to many riders with disabilities as they have no sitting balance

and often need to be strapped into their wheel-chairs. Exercises to be done by each individual should be varied as much as possible, to create enthusiasm.

The exercise portion of a lesson need not be long, nor must it always come in the same sequence, but it must be safe, planned work towards educational goals set by the special education teacher, beneficial and challenge the rider.

With all exercises the pony must be held correctly at the halt, walk or trot. Here are a few examples of RDA approved exercises:

1 Exercises for the body only:
Twist the trunk alternately from left to right with a) hands on hips, b) hands on shoulders and c) hands behind neck. Over trotting poles, with the pony at a walk, bend forward, rise up immediately after stepping over pole (**51**). This helps in the preparation of the first jump and for bending under branches.

2 For the arms and body combined (with the leg position constant):
Raise hand and touch toe a) on the same side, holding pommel, b) without holding and c) on opposite side. Touch parts of the pony, e.g. poll, elbow, hip, croup, ears, etc., a) holding pommel with other hand, b) not holding pommel.
Arms raised at shoulder level – swing to touch mane and tail (**52**) twisting trunk from left to right alternately.

52 *Touching the pony's tail, whilst holding the pommel.*

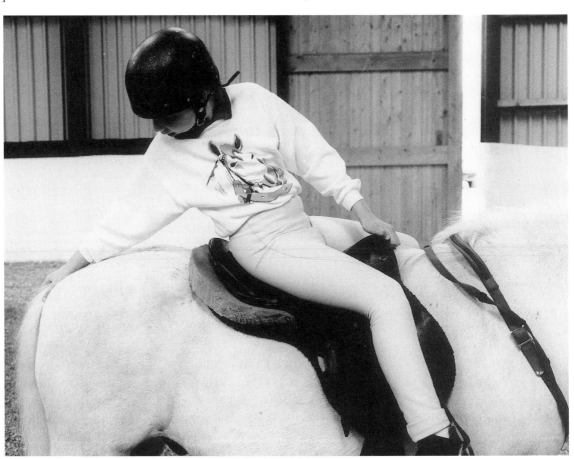

Twisting trunk and shoulders from left to right, letting arms swing floppily.

Progress by raising hands to shoulder height, hands towards pony's ears.
Both hands on shoulders a) stretch alternate arms sideways, forwards and upwards, b) stretch both arms sideways, forwards and upwards, and c) hands on head.

Progress for full co-ordination allowing one arm to start movement – other to follow.
Note: balance exercises are excellent for multiple sclerosis and paralysis and many other disabilities below the waist.

3 For the legs (arm and body positions remain constant):
Stretch legs downwards – hold, relax.
Stretch legs sideways – hold, relax (**53**).
Circle ankles in both directions.
At halt, without stirrups making rising trot movements, a) hold on to mane, b) no holding.

4 Head and neck:
Head turning left, then right.
Head circling – performed slowly, not more than three times.

5 Arms, hands and shoulders (54):
Wrist circling.
Arms swinging forward and backwards.
Arms circling – small and large circles.
Hands clapping in front – behind trunk.

The benefits of exercises include: stretching muscles, enhancing flexibility, improving balance, developing strength and relaxing and limbering areas of the body. Any exercise a student is asked to perform must not be harmful to him in any way, or aggravate his condition. A thorough knowledge of the disability of the individual is a must.

Exercises should be progressive, breaking them down into interesting components, adding a new component until the whole exercise can be performed well.

It should be stressed that when exercises are to be performed by disabled riders it is advisable to have the physiotherapist present.

For a larger list of exercises and detailed explanations, see RDA handbook.

Games

There are no set rules for games other than for all involved to have fun and thoroughly enjoy what they are doing.

Although a little low-key competition does stimulate the riders, especially mentally retarded riders, the emphasis must be on the rider's achievement on his own (without the aid of the helper). The rider's effort must be acknowledged straight away by the instructor and reinforced by the helper. Even if he comes in last, he may have made the biggest effort of the whole group. Generous reward spurs him on and gives him the determination to succeed.

Games can be played individually or as teams. The riders should enjoy what they are doing but must not be allowed to get too excited, as they may tend to do in 'race' situations.

The instructor and physiotherapist can devise games that best achieve the improvements desired in each individual and as a group. There should be plenty of 'props' available and, where possible, the school should be set up beforehand.

Safety rules must be obeyed and strongly enforced when games are being played, or else pandemonium can occur. The instructor should have a whistle around his neck, which when blown tells everyone that they *must* stand still *immediately*. This can help in the prevention of unnecessary accidents.

'Props' which are used in games can include: small beanbags, rings (made out of rubber, rope or small lengths of hose-pipe), tights filled with foam, cards with objects on and their 'real-life' matching object, posts, batons, clothes, buckets, plastic cups, cartons or yoghurt pots, serving spoons and plastic eggs, and letters.

There is an excellent list of games in the RDA handbook. Games can also be made up as long as the instructor and/or physiotherapist deems

53 *Legs stretched down and out.*

them to be safe. Here are a few examples of games played in a local RDA group.

Egg and spoon race:
The rider is given a serving spoon and positions the pony at the end of the school. On the command *go* he rides up to the other end of the school, collects an egg (plastic ball or small potato) from a helper or from the top of an oil drum, places it on his spoon, rides back down to the other end of the school, trying not to drop the egg, until he reaches a bucket on the ground

where he should try to deposit his egg. If he misses, he should be given the egg back to have another go, he may not dismount.

Treasure hunt:
Each rider has a 'grandmother' who has two cards, each with a drawing of an object and its name on one side, and the name only on the other side. The rider collects one card at a time, using either side according to ability, finds the object and returns it to 'grandmother'. The rider shouts agreed word when finished. This can be a race, if desired.

54 *Exercising arms, hands and shoulders.*

Dressing up race:

An old scarf and hat can be hung on a bending pole. The first rider puts these on and returns to the second rider who then returns clothes to the pole.

Postmen:

Here riders are encouraged to post letters or cards into a postbox, (any large box with a large slit will do). To encourage the riders, individualize their letters by using name labels or different colours, and for authenticity paint the postbox red.

Ordinary races can be played and races using bending poles are excellent in helping the rider to control the pony and increase his balance, in a situation where riding is incidental. Bending (weaving in and out of the poles) and walk, trot and canter races are probably the first races most able-bodied children participate in at gymkhanas. In fact, nearly all games which are played at gymkhanas may be suitable for riders with disabilities, and this is an area where many riders progress and compete in their own right. Party games can also be adapted for disabled riding, especially those using music, such as musical chairs, etc. where the rider should try to stop the pony on his own as soon as the music stops.

Dismounted activities – discussion

In some riding groups there are not enough ponies for all riders to ride at once. This is a good opportunity for one or two trained helpers to instruct in basic stable management. Even in a wheelchair, it is possible to learn about and practice grooming, unsaddling, points of the horse and feeding, however long it takes.

This type of instruction should be both informative and fun. It is a good idea to keep stable management workbooks for riders. In their own way (perhaps with help) they can describe their ponies, in pictures and/or words; what riding means to them and how they feel they have progressed each session.

Games such as word-searches, name the parts of the saddle/bridle, and matching games all help to encourage the rider to learn and will benefit him in the general management of horses. These can be designed to suit the individual.

This is also an excellent time to prepare individuals for the RDA proficiency tests. The type of things which can be taught are points of the horse, parts of tack, colours of ponies, markings of ponies, points of the hoof, grooming equipment and generally the basics of pony care and management. See Appendix.

7 DRIVING

Driving is an increasingly popular equestrian field for handicapped people, which in Great Britain has developed over the past fifteen years. It is also an area which in the United States is experiencing increasing growth and popularity. A wheelchair-bound individual knows few restraints when in a driving vehicle with an able-bodied driver. Specially built vehicles have been designed with ramps to enable the easy loading of a wheelchair. In one of these vehicles the disabled driver will feel safe and secure in his new-found freedom.

In Great Britain, driving groups are either extensions of established riding groups or can be new groups, solely devoted to driving. From a small beginning there has been a vast development in this area with approximately 100 driving groups catering for nearly 600 drivers.

In 1975 the first vehicle for the disabled was designed. There are now three types of vehicle, which have been developed from the ideas of disabled drivers. Purpose-built vehicles for driving for the disabled are those that have been designed to accommodate a wheelchair.

Whether disabled drivers are wheelchair bound or not, they must at all times be accompanied by an able-bodied driver, or 'whip' as he/she is known, as their safety is the most important factor to consider. Once driving, the drivers feel an exhilarating sense of freedom, enhancing their self-respect. 'A pony and vehicle can go where no wheelchair would dare.'

Driving is a sport in which it is possible for people with disabilities to compete on equal terms with the able-bodied (55). In 1988 there were two driving trials for the disabled and in 1989 there were three more at national events. There was also the first long-distance drive for disabled drivers which took place in the New Forest. There are currently other possibilities being considered for disabled drivers, bringing them right up to date with riding groups, and increasing the popularity of driving overall.

With these prospects we need to take a good hard look at **safety**. We must maximize the pleasure and minimize the risk – carriage driving at whatever level, is a risk sport and the best way of dealing with accidents is to prevent them from happening if we possibly can. The safe driving group is the well-trained group.[1]

Who drives?

As with riding, a disabled individual who wishes to drive must have medical consent, and if under eighteen must also have parental consent. Priority is given to individuals who are physically prevented from riding. Some handicaps make it impossible, or at least very painful, to ride, even if a person with such a handicap were to try it. Those that are permanently confined to a wheelchair are given a freedom which they may

55 *RDA drivers from the Diptford Group
compete in the 'hazards' at Killerton, Devon.
(Anne Swinscow)*

have never experienced before or that they may
have lost in the past.

Driving is becoming more popular among
riding groups for individuals who, because of
lack of muscle control, considerable body weight,
or advancing stages of disability, find they are
unable to ride astride. Driving is indicated for the
individual who does not have the physical,
psychological, or mental ability to be mounted.
In addition, it is encouraged for those who just
wish to enjoy this equestrian activity.

Driving safety

As with every aspect of riding for the disabled,
the first thing to consider when involving disabled individuals in driving is safety. The RDA
insists on a driving safety code, which is to be

adhered to at all times. The RDA safety code for
driving is as follows:

a) General

1 Driving on public highways is discouraged
and scurry driving and racing are not allowed.
However, convoy drives on private roads and
tracks, instructional drives and obstacle driving
are recommended.

2 Good-quality, well-fitting harness is essential.

3 Only turnouts which have been inspected and
approved may be used.

4 An experienced able-bodied whip, preferably
the owner or regular driver of the animal, must
ensure safety standards are maintained, including correct loading and unloading procedures.
There must be a minimum of two helpers to each

turnout.

5 Two sets of reins are needed for each vehicle, one for use by the disabled driver and the other to be used by the experienced whip in case of emergency or if the driver tires (**56**). A nylon headcollar should be put under the horse's bridle for a lead rein to be attached if and when necessary.

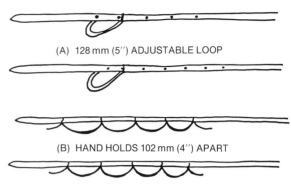

(A) 128 mm (5″) ADJUSTABLE LOOP

(B) HAND HOLDS 102 mm (4″) APART

57 *Looped reins (reproduced from RDA driving pamphlet)*

56 *The two sets of reins used for RDA driving. (Anne Swinscow)*

6 Looped reins as illustrated in figure **57** may be found useful.

b) Animals

1 All ponies/donkeys are inspected and approved for use in RDA driving groups. The ponies are known to the group organizer for at least one month prior to this inspection.

2 Ponies/donkeys are a) sound (legs and feet), are in good condition, are not under five years old or too old, are the right temperament and thoroughly reliable and obedient under *all* conditions; b) stand still for harnessing up, putting to, loading and unloading wheelchairs and whenever told to; c) responsive to aids and have good driving manners; d) not stallions.

3 They are driven regularly by competent whips in company and alone. They must have no objection to being overtaken from the rear, or to ponies in front of them. Riding can be included in their exercise.

4 Ponies from 11.2 hh to 13.2 hh are ideal, but there are exceptions.

c) Vehicles

1 RDA-approved vehicles, information on which can be obtained from RDA headquarters, are recommended for use.

2 Vehicles without a dashboard should not be used as they give no sense of security and it is possible to fall out in front of the wheels.

3 Vehicles with a ground clearance of approximately 45 cm (18 inches) are the most convenient for loading and unloading, and may be used on all types of ground.

4 Traditional and exercise vehicles may be used for ambulant disabled individuals, provided they are able to mount and dismount with the

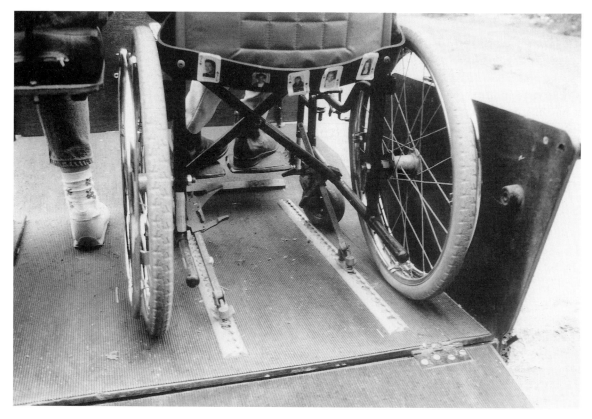

58 *A wheelchair securely fastened with 'Unwin Clamps' in a Jackson Darrent cart.*
(Anne Swinscow)

minimum of assistance. These vehicles must be inspected and approved individually.

5 Only one wheelchair in any one vehicle at one time is allowed. Electric wheelchairs should not be used. Wheelchairs must have brakes applied and be secured by quick release clamps or strap (**58**). It is recommended that the chair occupant wears a quick release safety belt at the discretion of the instructor in charge.

6 To maintain high standards of safety the following routine is used:

Before each session:
- Check shaft clamp bolts
- Check tyre pressures (25–30 psi)

- Visual check of body, bolts, etc.
- Check the bolts in the centre of the swingle tree. If one gives way it could cause a very nasty accident.
- Check all bolts with spanners.

Frequently:
- Wire spokes – tighten loose spokes, until just rattling. Do not over-tighten.
- Grease wheel bearings.
- Make sure that fastenings on vehicle ramps move and fix freely when ramps are lowered or raised.
- Check metal shafts – they can bend out of shape. A local metalworker can warm and reshape them.
- The woodwork should be painted and varnished regularly.
- Vehicles should be kept under cover. No vehicle is to be used that is not mechanically sound.

d) Inspectors

1 Two inspectors, who are on the list approved by the driving committee, will visit groups when they are ready for initial inspections. One or both will drive the ponies/donkeys.

2 No person with disabilities shall be allowed to drive an unapproved animal.

3 The inspectors will take note of the following:

a) Condition of ponies/donkeys, vehicles and harness.

b) Animal's handling ability and obedience.

c) Correct balancing and securing of vehicle (59).

d) The group's calmness and effiency in controlling numbers of people and animals.

e) The group's ability to cope with the unexpected.

f) Understanding of the points in the RDA Driving Pamphlet.

g) Understanding of the needs of handicapped people.

e) Helpers

An able-bodied companion whip is seated in the vehicle before the disabled driver gets in, controlling the pony/donkey with one pair of reins. He remains there until the disabled driver gets out.

A helper holds the pony or donkey's head at the start and on completion of the drive and whilst the handicapped driver gets in and out of the vehicle (whether in a wheelchair or on foot).

The able-bodied whip is in charge of the turnout, and will only release the helper when he/she is satisfied that all is in order before moving off.

Helpers must be able to cope with the unexpected. It is essential to have an instructor/experienced able-bodied whip in charge of the drive, watching the ponies, drivers and helpers at all times. Escorts on bicycles are invaluable.[2]

59 *A driving inspector testing a pony's reaction to a wheelchair being loaded at the inspection of Southfields Group. (Anne Swinscow)*

Driving helpers

Driving helpers have a crucial part to play in the safety of disabled people who come to the group to drive. If they abide by the safety code at all times there will be less chance of accidents occurring. If they are in the correct place at the correct time they can also prevent accidents. Accidents happen when rules are broken. A few rules to remember are:

Do not look back if the pony/donkey will not follow when being led. Where there is more than one vehicle in convoy, ensure a safe distance is kept between each and avoid making sharp turns. Gossiping between helpers causes accidents as concentration is affected. A cheerful, relaxed and confident helper will encourage drivers with disabilities to be relaxed and confident, helping them to really enjoy the activity. Enthusiasm on the part of the drivers is essential but it is possible they may become too excited. The helper must watch out for signs of mental and/or physical fatigue in drivers, and be prepared to stop. Above all else, the helper must remember that he is responsible for the driver's safety.

Driving facilities

There are at present in Great Britain limited suitable venues with good facilities and smooth places to ride. The ideal facility would be one with an indoor school large enough to drive in safely and flat enclosed outdoor areas. If an RDA driving group is to be successful and run safely, it needs to be able to supply certain needs for drivers with disabilities. A source of reliable, sound and well-cared-for ponies or donkeys which are in a fit state physically and mentally to do the job in hand, will need to be found; as will safe, well-fitting harness for them.

There must be a responsible person, who is an experienced whip, able to take charge of any drive that takes place. In addition, there should be a physiotherapist or occupational therapist willing to advise and assist the physically handi-

capped driver at regular intervals. For the mentally handicapped, the presence of a member of the staff of the hospital or school is essential.

The group also requires, as with riding groups, a team of responsible, hardworking and above all else, caring helpers who can deal with handicapped people and have some horse knowledge or are keen to learn.

Even when a group has established all of the above requirements, their standard will have to satisfy the regional chairman or person nominated by the regional committee to act on his/her behalf, and two driving inspectors as well.

Loading and unloading the wheelchair

The disabled driver can sometimes help more with getting a pony ready for a driving session than he can with preparing a pony for a riding session (**60**). There are many little things which need to be attended to, buckles which need to be done up on the harness, fastening the breast collar and girth, all of which are at wheelchair height. Grooming also can take place from a wheelchair. Those who are not wheelchair-bound can help with things higher or lower, such as bridling or cleaning the feet.

Once the pony has been groomed, it is time for 'harnessing up and putting to'; this is the correct term for putting on the harness and putting the pony into the driving vehicle. Drivers with disabilities should be encouraged as much as possible to help with this, as long as it is done safely, and there are adequate overseers. This is a good time for a final check of the harness, making sure all buckles are done up correctly. The vehicle must be balanced before the able-bodied whip gets in followed by the disabled driver. Once they are in, the vehicle should remain balanced. Weights can vary enormously between pairs of drivers; therefore, the weight which is to be loaded into the vehicle at any one time should be taken into consideration when looking to see if the vehicle is balanced before and after loading. A pony must never be overloaded with too much weight. Although he can pull more balanced weight than he can carry riding weight, there is a limit. If a group is to cater for a very heavy driver, it will need to have a larger, stockier pony or horse.

The loading of the vehicle comes next. A wheelchair-bound driver will need a ramp to

60 *The driver with a disability can take an active part in the preparation of pony and vehicle. (J. H. H. Peile)*

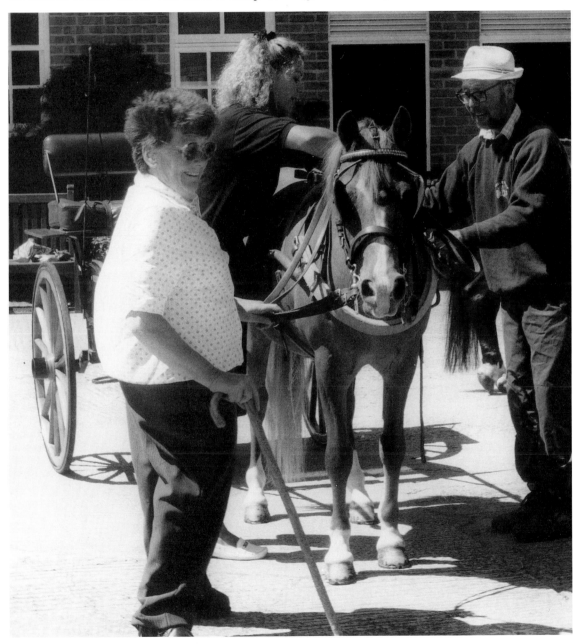

mount the vehicle. (Those who are not wheelchair-bound will simply mount the vehicle from a step at the side.) Once the ramp has been lowered, and the able-bodied whip is seated in the vehicle with control of it, as well as a helper at the head of the pony, the driver can be mounted. The driver must always wear a crash helmet and it is also advisable for him to be fastened into the wheelchair with a strap across the chest. There should be no fuss when loading and it must be done smoothly and quickly, to instil confidence into the driver (**61**). Loading a wheelchair and driver into a vehicle needs a minimum of two helpers and preferably three. Two to push from either side and one to hold the shafts is ideal (**62**). A heavy adult may also need someone to help pull the wheelchair. The wheelchair must not be tipped on to its back wheels as this will frighten

the driver, making him lose confidence. Once he is in position in the vehicle, the brakes of the wheelchair must be applied and the chair should be clamped into the vehicle. The ramp can then be closed.

Once driving, the able-bodied whip must remain in the vehicle at all times, ready to take control if necessary. There are many things disabled individuals can take part in when they are driving. They can participate in **dressage, cone courses (63), obstacle courses** or just pure **pleasure driving**. All of these activities can have the difficulty increased as the driver progresses, to help him improve still further. To drive the pony the driver should use his voice and reins. He may also use a whip around the area where a rider would squeeze with the legs. The whip can also be used on the shoulder to control

61 *A strong helper loading a wheelchair into a Jackson Darrent at the Tavistock Group, with able-bodied rider already seated and in control (Anne Swinscow)*

62 *The helper at the pony's head holds the shaft steady while the wheelchair is loaded. (Anne Swinscow)*

the direction of the pony.

Unloading is fairly simple, and again must be done quickly and efficiently. Once the ramp has been lowered the clamps can be removed and the wheelchair is simply wheeled down. (Those who are not wheelchair-bound will dismount from the vehicle using the side step.) Once again the disabled driver can help to unharness the pony and groom him down.

Driving qualifications

The RDA, as explained in Chapter 8, are now qualifying their riding instructors, yet there are not at present any RDA driving qualifications. However, this is not to say whips with or without

a disability cannot confirm their driving ability, because they are able to undertake the British Driving Society (BDS) qualifications.[3] The standard of these qualifications ranges from Test 1 preliminary – a simple but safe standard; Test 2 intermediate – where a more advanced knowledge and understanding and a higher practical ability is required; to Test 3 advanced – where a very high standard is required.

The safe driving group is the well trained driving group . . .

Safety starts at the top – firstly with the driving chairman and the driving committee, then down through the regional driving representatives and driving inspectors, on to group organizers and the helpers of whatever grade.

63 *Practising cone driving at the Diptford group, Devon. (Anne Swinscow)*

Regional driving representatives need *expertise and enthusiasm*, and they should aim at a good BDS qualification. Test 1 is a start, not a finish. It is hoped that driving representatives, inspectors and group organizers will be motivated to move on to tests 2 and 3. Certainly one member of each group should aim high – perhaps a new category could be introduced, that of group driving instructor. Regional driving representatives should have the time to visit their groups at least twice a season and motivate them to initiate training courses for helpers, *and these should be ongoing.*[4]

RDA driving conferences

RDA driving conferences are set up to enable those people involved in driving for the disabled to come along and look, listen, participate and learn from those who are experienced within a certain area.

After the preliminary registration and introduction, which is a common occurrence at any conference, the programme begins.

Each conference has a particular theme, for example at the 1989 RDA driving conference the theme was safety.

Many excellent lectures and demonstrations are organized for conferences set up by the RDA. Subjects scheduled, which follow a pattern based around the theme are usually packed with both practical and theoretical information. Guidelines and information are offered to a variety of delegates who may be helpers, able-bodied and/or disabled whips.

There are often opportunities for delegates to actively participate in demonstrations. Once the lectures and demonstrations are finished, there is a chance for the delegates to put questions to the 'experts' and for a discussion on matters demonstrated throughout the conference.

64 *RDA driving dressage:*
  a) *The arena*

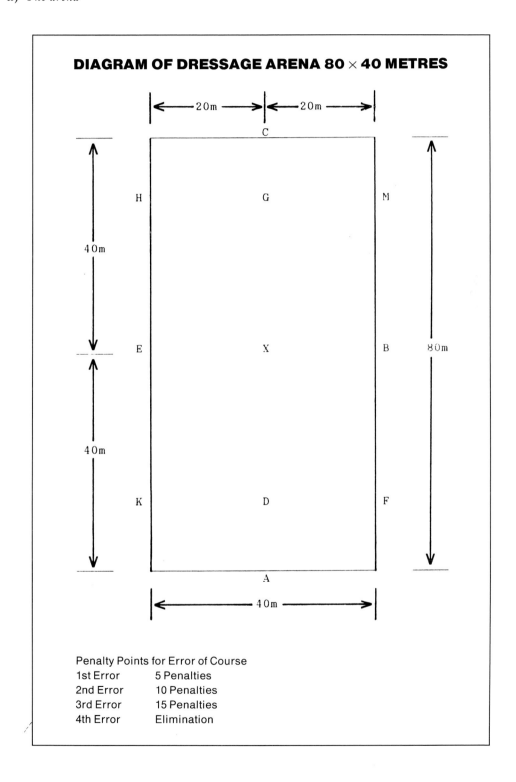

DIAGRAM OF DRESSAGE ARENA 80 × 40 METRES

Penalty Points for Error of Course
1st Error   5 Penalties
2nd Error   10 Penalties
3rd Error   15 Penalties
4th Error   Elimination

HORSE DRIVING TRIALS DRESSAGE TEST No. 5 – NOVICE STANDARD 1984
To be driven in 80 m × 40 m Arena for Singles and Pairs

64 *b The movements to be performed*

64c) *The dressage judges sheet (courtesy of BHS horse driving trials committee)*
Special equipment figs (reproduced from RDA Handbook by Gloria Dean)

The scale of marks is as follows:
10. Excellent   4. Insufficient
9. Very good   3. Fairly bad
8. Good   2. Bad
7. Fairly good   1. Very bad
6. Satisfactory   0. Not performed
5. Sufficient

THE BRITISH HORSE SOCIETY

HORSE DRIVING TRIALS DRESSAGE TEST No. 5 – NOVICE STANDARD 1984

100m x 40m for Teams and Tandems
80m x 40m for Singles and Pairs

COMPETITOR'S NUMBER ....

MOVEMENT			TO BE JUDGED	MARK 0 – 10	REMARKS
1.	A	Enter at working trot	Driving in on straight line		
	X	Halt, salute	Transition standing straight on the bit		
2.	XCMB	Working trot	Transition. Impulsion. Regularity. Position.		
3	BX	Half circle right 20m diameter	Accuracy of figure — Impulsion. Regularity		
	XE	Half circle left 20m diameter			
4.	EKAF	Working trot	Impulsion. Regularity. Position		
5.	FXH	Change rein and show a few lengthened strides	Impulsion. Regularity — Quality of Lengthening		
6.	HCMR	Working trot	Impulsion. Regularity. Position		
7.	RXVK	Walk	Transition. Impulsion. Regularity. Position		
8.	KADX	Walking trot	Transition. Impulsion. Regularity. Position		
9.	X	Halt 10 seconds. Immobility, Rein back 3 metres	Transition. Immobility. Straightness		
10.	X	Proceed at working trot	Transition. Regularity. Impulsion. Straightness		
11.	G	Halt, salute	Transition. Straightness. Standing on bit		
		Leave arena at working trot			
Collective marks:					
12.		Paces	Regularity and Freedom		
13.		Impulsion	Free forward movement		
14.		Obedience, lightness	Response to aids, Willing and without resistance		
15.		Driver	Use of aids, Handling of reins and whip. Position on box. Accuracy of figures		
			TOTAL		

Signature of Judge ....

Driving shows

Many disabled drivers take part in shows and competitions. Their participation in such events is often the culmination of many months of hard work and practice on the disabled driver's part. Often such participation will be in driving dressage. Here the driver will be required to give a show in front of a panel of judges. The show would include changes of pace, transitions, changes of rein, figures of eight, halt and rein back as shown in BHS driving dressage test 1984 novice standard No. 5 (**64a, b and c**). The task is a difficult one, yet the immense pleasure and feeling of accomplishment that the driver feels having finished his test, is reward in itself, no matter where he is placed. These drivers are very dedicated. They are aware that there is only one chance, not only of winning or being placed, but of proving that they can compete with the best. They go to enjoy themselves and they derive immense pleasure from the whole experience.

It is a professional activity, where drivers with disabilities show a professional attitude towards the whole business. They will be dressed as other drivers, men in their bowler hats, suits, aprons, gloves and buttonholes and women in their hats, jackets, skirt or trousers, apron and gloves. Their ponies are turned out impeccably with every thing sparkling and clean.

An able-bodied whip does accompany the driver and is allowed to hold the driving whip if the disabled driver is using looped reins. Many helpers are invaluable, and should be on hand the whole time, even when the show is being given. A suitably attired helper should accompany the vehicle into the arena on foot.

The judges look at the ability of the driver, seeing whether he shows confidence and commands his pony well with the aids and use of the voice. They look to see if the pony behaves and obeys the commands given by the driver. They also take into consideration the safety of the turnout and its suitability for the driver and pony, including the balance. The tack will also be inspected for condition, fit to the pony and cleanness. A smart turnout entering the arena will provide a good and lasting impression. The rest depends on the skill and awareness of the driver.

Driving representatives

Every region of the RDA is covered by a driving representative. In fact there are 16 representatives covering 18 regions. Some representatives may cover more than one region, whilst one region may have more than one representative.

The representatives are all experienced whips themselves; some competing in shows and driving trials at all different levels. They are, also, all members of the British Driving Society, which is the governing body for driving in Great Britain. Most representatives are experienced group organizers of established driving groups and most are on, or have been elected to, the driving committee of the RDA in the past.

This committee will be invited to visit different groups in the late spring, summer and early autumn, when groups are at their most active. As well as being required to carry out inspections of ponies, tack and vehicles, they are often invited to social events such as competitions and celebrations. They are often called upon to advise on problems which cannot be solved within the group itself. They are experienced and their advice is valuable.

As explained in the driving safety code, the representative is needed to inspect and approve a new driving group. However, before the group is ready for inspection he will help to fill in the correct forms, decide on the best venue, the safest harness and how to recruit helpers etc., all of which must be correct before the inspection day.

Any matter concerning driving for the disabled in any particular region concerns that region's representative, whether there be one or ten groups within that one region. Therefore, the representative must be available to travel about the region, giving help when and where needed.

The job is an enjoyable one, providing pleasure-able opportunities to meet many admirable people.

National driving representation

In Great Britain, the driving committee of the RDA and the British Driving Society, of which there is a representative involved with the RDA committee, are the two associations concerned with driving for the disabled. The RDA driving committee exercises control over all driving activities within the association and the BDS assists and advises when and where necessary. The BDS founded the Sanders Watney Disabled Driving Trust, which is a registered charity providing horse driving activities for people with severe disabilities. The RDA driving committee has established safety standards and driving guidelines to assist able-bodied/disabled whips and helpers in all aspects relating to driving for people with disabilities, as well as producing the RDA driving pamphlet and hints for helpers leaflet.

In the United States, the National Association for Driving for the Disabled (NADD),[5] which is a member of NARHA, and the NARHA driving committee, which works closely with NADD, are the two associations concerned with driving for people with disabilities.

While individuals with disabilities have been competing in driving for the disabled events as well as open events for the past few years, these associations are now seeking to establish stan-dards and guidelines to assist drivers with dis-abilities in all aspects of recreational driving and competitive driving. They conduct clinics for driving for people with disabilities, certify in-structors, assist drivers in competitions, and establish guidelines and standards for driving for the disabled competitions.

In addition, NADD is working with business and community groups and government agencies on a national basis to promote equine-related recreation and therapy through driving. From co-sponsoring seminars and lectures to working with equine research centres, this organization is committed to developing carriage driving pro-grammes to their fullest potential.

The RDA and NARHA driving committees promote driving through their associations' member groups, encouraging the formation of new groups and assisting in the expansion of existing riding groups to accommodate driving. They are responsible for the inspection of all driving groups, including vehicles, ponies etc. and also encourage competition.

65 *Bruce Grosvenor, of Oldwick, NJ, USA, is a quadriplegic who has chosen to drive in a slightly modified four-wheeled trap. Pictured here with his wife, Candy, driving his Morgan 'TF's Excaliber' at the Annual Champagne Coaching Weekend in Saratoga Springs, NY, USA. (photograph courtesy of Sue Greenall, Thorny Hills Farm, Fogelsville, PA, USA)*

There are approximately 100 RDA driving groups in Great Britain, catering for roughly 600 drivers. There are approximately 25–30 programmes for the disabled, conducting driving activities for individuals with disabilities in the United States. Both two- and four-wheeled vehicles are being used in these activities. Activities being conducted currently include pleasure driving, pleasure shows, combined driving events at the lower level, dressage, invitational drives, promotional drives and exhibition driving.

While the roots of driving for the disabled in America stem from Great Britain and the Continent, the design or modification of traditional vehicles for use in American programmes may have a distinct American flavour (65). In one instance, a man with a disability uses a three-wheeled cart that is actually pushed by the horse, rather than pulled.

In the 1990s it is hoped by all involved in driving for the disabled that the number of riding-for-the-disabled groups which offer driving will increase. Additionally it is hoped that driving will be promoted by the associations as less of an elitist activity. Perhaps most important of all, it is hoped that the 1990s will see disabled drivers join regular driving events and groups.

8 TRAINING, EXAMINATIONS AND TESTS

The status of certification

An instructor in an RDA group does not at present have to hold any formal instructor qualifications. However, the British Horse Society does certify riding instructors and, as stated before, the standard of teaching should be of the standard of a BHS preliminary teaching certificate. The RDA has now launched 'The Training Programme', for group instructors, to enable instructors to become qualified in riding for the disabled.

Unlike Great Britain, the United States has no single equestrian governing body which accredits riding institutions and certifies riding instructors. The American Horse Show Association provides standards in some areas of the equestrian world, and certain states across the country do license stables and riding establishments. But these activities are not carried out on a national basis within one national organization. It is too large a country, with too many different types of equine and equestrian programmes, to be able to effectively regulate the equestrian world.

In the United Kingdom, instructors must have passed BHS examinations before they can become qualified instructors and be eligible to teach riding students. They may then go on to take the RDA instructor's examinations to become recognized teachers of disabled riders. However, in the United States it is possible for anyone to say he or she is a riding instructor, and this individual may, if he so chooses, begin calling himself a riding instructor and taking riding students. For many years there were individuals who thought that to be a therapeutic riding instructor was less demanding than being a regular riding instructor. Thus, therapeutic riding instructors often had no background in teaching riding prior to their entering this vocation.

Today, however, this picture is changing. The North American Riding for the Handicapped Association has been certifying therapeutic riding instructors since the late 1970s, and this certification programme was revised in 1989–90.

The current NARHA instructor certification programme provides standards and a process for those who wish to obtain professional certification. Basic and advanced certificates are being awarded to those individuals who meet the appropriate qualifications. The basic level of certificate bears the label Certified Instructor. This individual is a knowledgeable horse-person and is well-versed in disabilities and their relation to riding. He or she must show evidence of being able to conduct a safe and challenging lesson for handicapped riders. The advanced certificate bears the label Master Instructor. This instructor has a strong background in horsemanship and a thorough knowledge of the disabilities and their relationship to riding. At this level, the individual can step into any teaching situation in the therapeutic riding field and take charge effectively. At this level the individual can also educate and train other therapeutic riding instructors.

Implementation of certification programmes

In Great Britain

The RDA Instructors' Assessment and Examination training programme for group instructors offers an exciting challenge for any group instructor, and will also structure and improve every instructor's teaching technique which, of course, will have an immediate and direct benefit on disabled riders.

Participation in the assessment or examination is entirely voluntary, although the RDA training committee does encourage every instructor to take part.

The purpose of the RDA Instructors' Examination is to produce all-round experienced instructors, who are able to instruct outside their own groups and in unfamiliar surroundings, with initiative. Passing the examination entails hard work and dedication. The work involved will widen the knowledge and experience of candidates and help them to teach better in both their own groups and in unusual situations. Experience with many types of handicaps and a variety of age groups is essential. The RDA has set out guidelines to help potential candidates, which cover a) instructing b) medical and physiotherapy knowledge c) RDA knowledge d) stable management e) RDA instructor's log book f) draft exam programme and suggested reading. These will make sure that each potential candidate is conversant with the outline programme and aware of the different sections of the examinations.

The Group Instructors' Assessment Syllabus, for which, if successful, candidates will be awarded a certificate, is initially to be carried out within the group base by a county instructor;

and, if, recommended, the group instructor may apply to attend a full assessment organized on a national basis.

The assessment is based on the RDA Handbook, the BHS Instructor's Handbook and the Manual of Horsemanship and will be linked to levels of horse care and management for the horse industry – BHS Stage 1 and 2; details of which are available from the British Horse Society.

The minimum age for the examination is 19 years and copies of the following must accompany all applications to the RDA:

1   A letter of approval signed by the regional instructor.

2   A log book, counter-signed by the regional instructor or county instructor, giving details of the candidate's experience with riders with and without disabilities. This must include a minimum of 50 hours teaching of handicapped riders and show that the candidate has attended at least one regional training day.

3   A current St John's or Red Cross first aid certificate.

Candidates may be assessed in giving a class lesson to four or more handicapped riders and in giving an individual lesson to a handicapped rider. This may be on or off a lead line, or may be a lunge lesson or dismounted activity. They may also be assessed in discussion. The points of knowledge and understanding that will be considered by the assessors during the lesson or discussion will be:

1   **Ride control.** Rapport with riders and helpers. Effective use of helpers. Short- and long-term goals for each rider. Progression through the lesson. Ability to make the lesson fun.

2   **Leading and assisting.** Training and improving leaders and helpers. Tactful control and briefing of helpers.

3   **Lifting and assisting riders to mount** from the ground, using a ramp or mounting block. The ability to delegate in order to carry out mounting and dismounting without delay.

4 Suitability of horses and ponies and an ability to allocate them in the best interests and to the advantage of the riders. The welfare and management of the horses/ponies.

5 a) The fit, care and **upkeep of tack.**

b) Modifications to tack that can be helpful.

6 Disabilities and the benefits that can be achieved through riding.

7 The consideration of safety: for riders, ponies/horses and helpers.

8 The structure of an RDA group, including insurance, and its place within the association.

9 What help can be obtained from county and regional level for the group.

For the Group Instructor's Examination all of the above points apply, and in addition the candidate must have already passed the **BHS Preliminary Teaching Test.** The examination is designed to be within the reach of the average experienced group instructor. As far as possible the examination will relate closely to the normal group conditions of the candidate's own group and questions will refer to his or her particular experiences or disability. The candidate must show that he/she is capable of instructing at group level with a sound practical knowledge.

The candidate's log book should also show a minimum of 50 hours teaching of handicapped riders, preferably with more than one group, which should show at least 15 hours experience with physically handicapped riders and 15 hours with mentally handicapped riders. The candidate must also have attended a regional training day.

Candidates will be examined on the same points as in the assessment and additionally on the organization and running of an RDA group, how and from where to obtain helpers, understanding the importance of and co-operation with the physiotherapist and/or special school teacher within the group, a basic knowledge of special equipment that can be helpful to very severely handicapped riders and a knowledge of accident procedure and first aid.

In the United States

To implement a certification programme in a country as large as the United States, NARHA requires candidates at the certified instructor level to meet certain criteria and, in addition, to submit a video-tape of their riding ability and also their ability to instruct riders with disabilities. The video must include a segment of instruction of riders without disabilities. In addition, these candidates must pass a written examination covering stable management, as well as disabilities, particularly as they relate to riding activities. An additional requirement for these candidates would be proof of continuing education; for example, attending a NARHA educational workshop or annual conference.

For the Master Instructor level of certification, all of the above mentioned criteria are needed, and in addition, the candidate must complete an on-site examination. Here the candidate is required to ride in front of an assessor, and demonstrate not only a more advanced level of horsemanship, but also more knowledge and skills in the area of stable management. This individual is also required to conduct an on-site therapeutic riding lesson containing, of course, unknown students, horses and helpers.

The overall goals of designing such a comprehensive instructor certification programme include making the vocation more professional and providing the handicapped students with better and more nationally consistent service.

For physiotherapists

The Special Interest Section (SIS) of the CSP, which is now the ACPRD, was formed in 1970. The idea behind establishing this special section was to bring together all physiotherapists interested in riding for the disabled. There is, however, a shortage of physiotherapists who have the necessary skills required for riding therapy work. The ACPRD recognizes this and is working hard to train more physiotherapists and to establish their role within riding for the disabled

(66a and b). A few occupational therapists are working in RDA and are accepted as affiliated members of the ACPRD.

The recruitment of physiotherapists who already work in RDA but who are not members of the ACPRD and the introduction of new therapists into this field are two of the main aims of the ACPRD. They are also responsible for postgraduate training leading to the use of riding as a therapy and assist in RDA training schemes.

It is accepted that physiotherapists must be equipped to play a full part in the RDA and that there is a real need to develop a proper qualification, with accepted levels of training. The ACPRD has introduced a qualification for physiotherapists which complements the RDA instructor's examination. It is hoped that this will satisfy the need for a higher level of qualification, so that the instructor and physiotherapist can combine their skills, understanding each other at this higher level.

A two-level training programme called 'The Horse in Rehabilitation', is being developed and organized by the ACPRD. Level I, entitled 'The Horse', is designed to introduce the physiotherapist to the potential of using the horse as a therapeutic agent, to give the physiotherapist an opportunity to gain horse knowledge and improve riding ability, and to introduce the practical aspects of riding for the disabled. Level II, 'The Disabled Rider', will give the physiotherapist an insight into the therapeutic effects of riding. A training committee appointed by the ACPRD is developing the course.

66 *A qualified physiotherapist, and one who is experienced in RDA work, demonstrates a) the 'arm over thigh and ankle hold' and b) (right) the 'knee hold', as an example of the kind of training involved in 'The Horse in Rehabilitation' programme.*

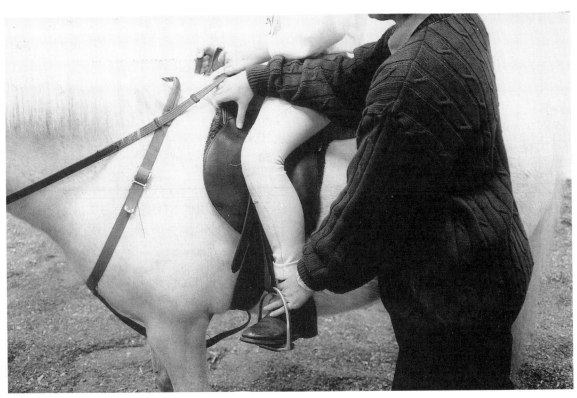

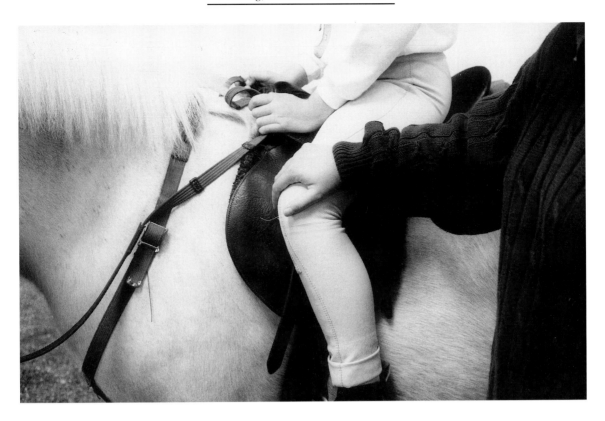

The Fortune Centre Of Riding Therapy

The Fortune Centre is a registered charity which is not run for profit. It aims to:

1a) Extend the education of slow-learning school leavers and those with emotional and behavioural difficulties.

b) Offer occupational training to young people who have experienced problems bridging the gap between school and the world of work

by a two-year *Further Education through Horsemastership* programme, fostering the development of life and social skills.

2 Introduce to young people the working concept of training alongside those less able than themselves, by a one-year foundation course culminating in the British Horse Society Assist-ant Instructor's Examination. This qualification is a pre-requisite for those wishing to train as riding therapists.

3a) Through short courses for allied professionals, promote an increased understanding of the working practice of riding therapy.

b) By a two-year residential course, train mature and/or graduate professionals as full-time riding therapists.

4 Provide for the long-term care of those whose disability prevents them entering employment, by supporting an 'Ostler' Home; demonstrating the value of horses in the lives of individuals to whom they offer an unprecedented opportunity for worthwhile occupation.

5 Offer a riding facility for groups of handicapped children from local schools on a once a week basis, by the maintenance of a member group of the RDA.

Training hippotherapists in the United States

A project to train a model group of hippotherapy specialists and to develop educational curricula in the field was designed by Therapeutic Riding Services of Baltimore, MD, in August of 1986. This project, which is being conducted in co-operation with the Delta Society of Renton, WA, and with the encouragement of NARHA, is now in its third phase: testing curriculum.

In the first phase of the hippotherapy curriculum development project, a core group of 43 United States and Canadian physical and occupational therapists practising individualized types of hippotherapy was identified and surveyed. From this group a smaller group of 19 therapists was selected to attend an intensive training programme at the Rommel-Klinik in Wildbad, West Germany (October 1987). This clinic is internationally famous for its application of the horse as a rehabilitation tool for patients with movement disorders. At the Rommel-Klinik, classic hippotherapy is practised on a daily basis. Here, too, hippotherapist training courses for the German National Association for Therapeutic Riding are conducted on a quarterly basis. To date over 750 German physical therapists have received their post-graduate diplomas in the speciality of hippotherapy. The German hippotherapy training course was specifically redesigned to meet the need of the United States and Canadian therapists.

As an integral part of the programme in Germany, Dr Loretta Rowley, PhD, project Curriculum Development Specialist, conducted DACUM sessions with the group. DACUM is a word used to describe a specific curriculum development process which originated at the Ohio State University in 1976. Under Dr Rowley's guidance, using the DACUM process, the group identified competencies, duties and tasks specifically related to hippotherapy. A working chart of these has now been compiled and validated (67). The duties and tasks identified on this chart have been used to design the teaching modules of the hippotherapy training curriculum.

As a result of studying classical hippotherapy in Germany, and using the DACUM process, four prototype curricula in hippotherapy have been designed and are being tested:

1   A three-to six-hour educational seminar for physicians and medical specialists.

2   A three- to four-day educational and experimental workshop for allied health professionals seeking further information on hippotherapy.

3   A two- to three-hour educational unit for undergraduate PT/OTs to learn about hippotherapy as an adjunct treatment.

4   A three- to four-week training programme for post graduated PT/OTs to become hippotherapy practitioners.

The tasks of the hippotherapy Curriculum Development Project for the 1990s are numerous. Major steps to be taken during this decade include the development and implementation of standards for therapists practising in this emerging field. A hippotherapist certification process will also need to be developed. Many therapists involved in the use of the horse as a therapeutic tool have expressed a desire to form a special-interest group, to specifically address the issues within this field of practice. Finally, to support the efficiency of the horse as a physiotherapeutic tool, a sound programme of research must be designed and implemented.

There is no established training programme for hippotherapists in the UK or any equivalent standard for therapists practising in this area. British physiotherapists are becoming increasingly excited about the potential of hippotherapy. It is practised in Britain and the number of therapists doing it is growing fast. At a guess there are probably about 20 RDA groups in which hippotherapy is practised but there is a real desire amongst physiotherapists for more training in this field and many are eager to start.

67 *The Hippotherapist Profile, a chart of duties and tasks performed by a hippotherapist (developed in 1988 by a group of physical and occupational therapists from the US and Canada, Romley Educational Consulting, Tucson, AZ)*

HIPPOTHERAPIST PROFILE ©

Duties — Tasks

A — Program Administration
- A.1 Select suitable facility
- A.2 Establish liaison with Board of Directors
- A.3 Negotiate contract
- A.4 Establish salary guidelines
- A.5 Approve policies and procedures
- A.6 Recruit therapy team
- A.7 Supervise therapy team
- A.8 Implement fee schedule
- A.9 Obtain program insurance
- A.10 Schedule treatment sessions
- A.11 Market hippotherapy
- A.12 Maintain record keeping system
- A.13 Establish 3rd party reimbursement
- A.14 Develop proposals to obtain funding
- A.15 Coordinate with state & national associations
- A.16 Evaluate program

B — Patient Care
- B.1 Practice program safety
- B.2 Implement emergency plan
- B.3 Consult with referral services
- B.4 Screen patient
- B.5 Place patient
- B.6 Determine program equipment needs
- B.7 Evaluate patient
- B.8 Develop treatment plan
- B.9 Coordinate hippotherapy with other programs
- B.10 Coordinate therapy team
- B.11 Assess horse suitability for patient
- B.12 Select equipment for patient
- B.13 Treat patient
- B.14 Interpret treatment results
- B.15 Maintain patient records
- B.16 Communicate with parents/professionals
- B.17 Discharge patient

C — Equine Skills
- C.1 Participate in horse selection
- C.2 Participate in horse training
- C.3 Participate in horse management
- C.4 Select horse equipment
- C.5 Maintain horse equipment

D — Professional Development
- D.1 Utilize dressage theory
- D.2 Demonstrate dressage skills
- D.3 Demonstrate therapeutic lunge-ing proficiency
- D.4 Demonstrate long-reining proficiency
- D.5 Demonstrate back-riding proficiency
- D.6 Develop innovative treatment techniques
- D.7 Maintain professional insurance
- D.8 Participate in professional organizations/conferences
- D.9 Participate in continuing education
- D.10 Participate in review process
- D.11 Develop and participate in research

E — Education
- E.1 Develop training manual
- E.2 Train therapy team
- E.3 Conduct in-service training
- E.4 Conduct therapy student training
- E.5 Act as consultant
- E.6 Develop public awareness
- E.7 Video tape treatment session

For riders with disabilities

Proficiency tests in riding and stable management

There are proficiency tests in seven grades available to disabled riders. They are divided into two parts: section A covers theory and dismounted activities, whilst section B covers riding ability and knowledge. Candidates may pass either section A or section B and receive a certificate. For example, Grade I, where candidates will be awarded with a blue badge on completion of both parts, is a very basic test. For section A candidates should have a very simple knowledge of the points of the pony, know some parts of the bridle and know how, and when, to give a reward. For section B candidates should be able to sit happily, maintaining position. Help is allowed as necessary at halt, walk and changes of direction.

The tests get more difficult as the rider's ability increases. The certificates test the candidates in progressively greater depth, extending the range tested. For example, when candidates reach Grade IV standard they will, for section A:

1   Show some understanding of pony behaviour and show some horse sense in approach and handling.

2   Know basic foods for a stable-kept pony, and the routine for watering.

3   Know how to groom a stable-kept pony and name additional grooming kit items required.

4   Know the reasons for taking the pony to the farrier.

5   Know the essential care of saddlery and be able to put on a saddle and bridle, with assistance if necessary.

6   Know how to put on a headcollar, lead in hand and recognize if a pony is correctly tied up.

For section B, their riding ability should show them to be able to:

1   Ride unaided, off a lead line in an enclosed space. Show a practical seat, as far as disability allows, at walk and trot and attempt to apply correct aids.

2   Show control at walk by demonstrating, on an obliging pony, changes of rein, 10 m and 20 m circles.

3   Jump a very low fence (this is at the instructor's and examiner's discretion, and is not compulsory).

Once riders have passed grade IV they can then go on to the Bronze, Silver and Gold awards which require the rider to have good riding skills and show sound knowledge of horse management. For example, for the Gold Award, a rider should be able to ride independently in varying circumstances and be able to jump a small course of fences, minimum height 60 centimetres (2 foot) (**68a and b**). He should also be able to demonstrate or explain how to 'turn out' a horse for show and explain the structure of the horse's foot and different shoeing methods, as well as many other things.

There are also proficiency tests for disabled drivers which follow the same pattern, except instead of riding ability being assessed the candidates driving ability is assessed. The areas to be tested will, of course, be related to driving. Taking Grade III as an example (where candidate's disability makes practical demonstration impossible he must be capable of explaining correct procedure):

Section A Theory – Know a little about pony/donkey behaviour. Have a wider knowledge of looking after an animal, care of harness, use of grooming kit, reason for shoeing, main foods used, etc., watering.

Have elementary knowledge of different types of vehicles and their uses. Have a wider understanding of the correct fit of harness. Know a little of the alternative harness which may be used. Understand the use of the whip.

68 *(right) As a rider progresses through the tests, jumping becomes a requirement, firstly a) with assistance and then b) without assistance (a and b Don Corcoran)*

Section B Practical ability – Give a practical demonstration of section A, as required, or explain correct procedure.

Section C Driving ability – The candidate must be able to understand the correct adjustment of wheelchair for balance, etc., and fastenings required.

The candidate should be able to demonstrate a simple 'set' course, including turns through bollards, trot down a line of bending poles, changes of direction with correct signals where possible.

69 A rider turned out smartly ready for her participation in a handy pony event away from home.

Participation in activities away from home

The RDA tries to integrate with both pony and riding clubs and a number of the more proficient riders within the RDA do take part in championships and pairs competitions (**69**). A number of RDA riders also attend pony club camps, where they take part in many different activities in a very informal, fun atmosphere.

There are many activities organized for disabled riders and the provision of riding holidays

is one of the major pursuits of the RDA. On these holidays disabled riders will have the chance to join in activities other than riding. Riders will also have the oportunity to try dressage, jumping, hacks and the like, as long as they are able and willing to try. Many helpers are involved in these holidays, so that high safety standards are maintained away from home as well.

The assisted training scheme for individual RDA riders

In 1987, from 17 riders who had all competed successfully in RDA National Dressage Championships held each year since 1981, the RDA selected seven adult riders to compete in the first world championships in Sweden. During the six months prior to the event, the riders received special coaching from Miss Pat Manning. As a result of their talents and of the special training received, the riders achieved incredible heights, and returned home with two gold medals and many placings in a strong field of 55 competitors from eight countries, to their, their coaches' and the RDA's credit (**70**).

> As a result of this venture we are more than ever convinced that there is a future in competitive dressage for many more of our riders who have some ability, but above all the desire, to excel in this field. We are well aware that this will only be a small percentage of the total number of RDA riders.
>
> We recognize the needs of the majority who may never learn to ride at all but for whom the benefits to be derived from sitting on a pony can be far-reaching.
>
> At the other end of the scale we recognize the needs of those who can learn to ride independently, and who struggle to free themselves from the disabled label. Given the opportunity they will serve as an example of what can be achieved and will be good ambassadors for the RDA movement. (RDA)

The plan of the scheme is to offer assisted

70 *Helen Scott competing at the First World Dressage Championships in Sweden, where she finished sixth in the Open Championship. She was only acquainted with the horse on the previous day. (photo: Express and Star)*

training places to individual RDA riders to enable them to progress beyond the scope of the average RDA group (**71**). Initially this will be for training on the flat in the field of dressage and where possible the riders will take part in open competition. However, it might be possible to include showjumping, eventing and driving at a later stage.

71 *Alysa Seals, a rider with a spinal abnormality, jumping her favourite horse, All Smiles, at the 1st Annual Therapeutic and Recreational Riding Center, Inc., Benefit Horse Show at Foxfield Farm in Woodbine, MD. (Karen A. Seals)*

Like Always

Like Always (called LA for short by her students) has worked for the past 18 years with mentally and physically handicapped riders at the Cheff Center for the Handicapped, in Augusta, Michigan. During her years of service and loyalty, Like Always has learned to adapt to the special needs of her riders.

For the rider with tight adductors, she stands quietly at the ramp or by the mounting block, while the rider's muscles slowly adjust to the stretch of being astride a horse. For those who have trouble with balance, such as leg amputees and spina bifida riders, she adjusts her speed and works at keeping them centred in the saddle. If they should slip, she stops immediately to give them time to readjust themselves. For the beginner and physically impaired rider, she helps by responding to voice commands as well as hand and leg aids.

Temperament is the most important consideration in using a horse for handicapped riders. 'No one could ask for a horse with a better disposition than LA,' says Cheff's physical therapy assistant, Teri Keupfer. 'She is always friendly and loving, eager for attention and affection, and most of all, patient. No matter how many times she's knocked by crutches or wheelchairs, bumped by flaccid legs or braces, or hit by balls and rings during our games, she never overreacts and is always forgiving.'

Over the years, LA has carried hundreds of physically challenged youngsters and adults without complaint. Now semi-retired, LA no longer carries the heavier students, although they continue to ask for her as she is their favourite.

There have been other horses as well liked as LA at the Cheff Center, but none that could match her overall ability to assist others in learning to ride. 'It takes a very special horse to keep riding as a positive experience for the handicapped individual,' notes Ms Keupfer. 'And I believe Like Always is one of those exceptional animals.'

9 THE ROLE OF THE ASSOCIATIONS

Aims and objectives of the RDA

The Riding for the Disabled Association is the only governing body for disabled riding in the United Kingdom. It is not a group of people who claim to perform miracles, nor is it medically orientated; yet its aim is very clear and very far-reaching. 'Our aim, in simple terms, is to provide the opportunity of riding or driving to people with disabilities who might benefit in their general health and well-being.' (RDA)

In addition to this main aim, the association, through the medical profession, aims to research into the benefits of riding for people with disabilities. It also strives to enlist and/or maintain the continued support of the British Horse Society, ministries, local authorities and all other interested bodies. It has the power to raise funds for the object of the association and to form or assist in forming clubs of supporters and friends of the association and to assist them in raising funds for the object of the association.

Structure of the RDA

The RDA is a registered charity. It is an association made up of nearly 700 member groups, catering for approximately 23,500 riders and drivers (72). These member groups elect a representative for each region to become members of the council of the association. This person becomes the regional chairman, representing his region in all matters pertaining to riding for the disabled. Each region has a committee, made up of a county chairman within the region, a regional instructor, a regional physiotherapist and other advisers: this committee is directed by the regional chairman. Regional representation is then broken down into county representation. At this level the county chairman and county instructor provide direct help to the many member groups. The council's decision to decentralize to the regions in this way was made so that the association, which was increasing at an enormous rate, could keep in touch with each single member group and spread the administration at this local level. It also decided that local affairs are best handled by the local people who are in touch with their community and its own specific needs. It also recognized that local people who gave money to the association appreciated seeing their money being put to local use, benefiting individuals with disabilities in their own area.

The RDA council has the advice of the medical and paramedical professions; representatives of the British Horse Society, British Veterinary Association, Chartered Society of Physiotherapy, British Orthopaedic Association, British Association of Occupational Therapists, Royal Association for Disability and Rehabilitation, British Red Cross Society, Spastics Society, National Council for Special Education, Department of Education and Science and

72 *Structure of the RDA*

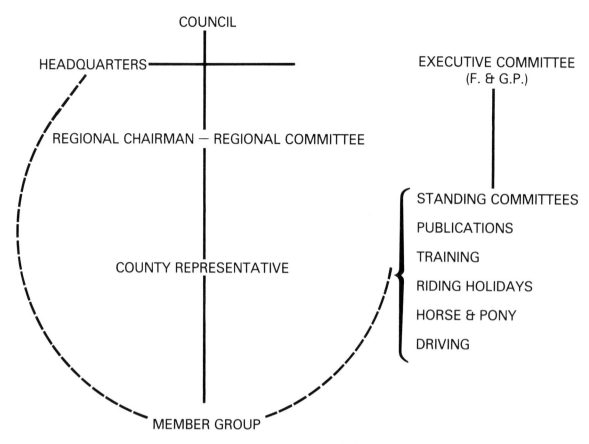

COUNCIL

HEADQUARTERS

EXECUTIVE COMMITTEE
(F. & G.P.)

REGIONAL CHAIRMAN — REGIONAL COMMITTEE

STANDING COMMITTEES

PUBLICATIONS

TRAINING

RIDING HOLIDAYS

HORSE & PONY

DRIVING

COUNTY REPRESENTATIVE

MEMBER GROUP

73 *The logo of the RDA*

Sports Council are on the RDA council. The duties and responsibilities of the council are many and widespread, yet through its standing committees it can keep in touch with every single member group, assisting and advising promptly and efficiently, when and where needed.

The administration of the RDA is carried out by a small workforce at RDA headquarters, situated at the National Agricultural Centre at Stoneleigh, Warwickshire. The director of the association, Mr J. R. Moss, and the headquarters staff are the only salaried personnel within the RDA movement. The principal role of head-quarters is to co-ordinate the activities of the council, standing committees and member groups. Additionally, it undertakes the central administration of the association, liaison with other medical, equestrian and national bodies, finance, insurance and fundraising. The logo of the Riding for the Disabled Association (73) appears on all of the association's literature and information. It represents the association's wish to promote equine activities for disabled people.

The management committee is appointed by the council, to – amongst other responsibilities –

conduct the general administration of the association as delegated by the council and to supervise and control finance.

Standing committees are appointed by the council to work in various fields. These committees report to the council through the management committee (74). These committees have executive powers within their own areas.

74 *Organization chart*

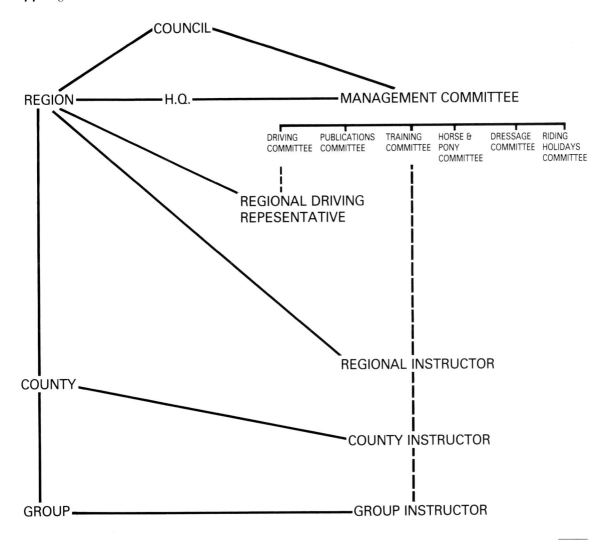

Full member groups; provisional member groups

The association's member groups provide riding and/or driving for physically and/or mentally handicapped people, adults and children alike. There are large purpose-built centres and there are small groups, but every member group is of vital importance to the object of the RDA.

The groups are bound together to give them the strength and inspiration which comes from a unity of purpose; to enable them to learn from each other; to give them as an association a loud, clear voice which can be heard in the hubbub of the modern world; to give them the advantages of Royal Patronage and the benefits of nationwide recognition. Organizations for disabled riders from many parts of the world are affiliated to the Riding for the Disabled Association. (RDA Handbook)

Member groups are divided into 18 regions: 12 in England, three in Scotland, two in Wales and one in Northern Ireland. Membership of the association is open to groups of persons regularly engaged locally in providing riding or driving for people with disabilities. It falls into two categories: 1) Provisional Membership 2) Full Membership.

A group will be recommended for provisional membership, which will not normally last for more than one year, by the regional chairman, with consultation with the regional instructor. Groups will be visited and inspected, with a view to recommendation. A provisional group may apply for full membership, through the regional chairman at any time on production of a copy of its constitution.

How member groups are organized

Each new group must set up a management committee, which should consist of at least a Chairman, Honorary Treasurer and Honorary Secretary. The responsibility for managing the group will fall on their and a few other elected peoples' shoulders. A shared team effort will produce the best results.

This management committee, amongst other duties, will be responsible for the appointment of a group instructor, a group organizer, a group physiotherapist or occupational therapist, the training of helpers and the provision of riding facilities including suitable ponies etc.

The instructor to be appointed must comply with the requirements of the RDA. Where physically handicapped individuals are to be catered for, the services of a physical or occupational therapist must be sought. It is essential, when mentally handicapped individuals are attending riding sessions, for a member of the staff of their school/centre or hospital to be present. The committee should also organize a nucleus of responsible helpers, and a complete first aid kit, which must be readily accessible at all times to all persons, and an accident book where all accidents and incidents must be recorded. The medical consent for riders to ride must be sought from the doctor through the committee, and up-to-date records of every rider must be kept. The committee will also be responsible for the implementation of fundraising for group needs.

Who decides to start up a new group and who can?

The setting-up of a new group can be undertaken by anyone who has a genuine desire to help handicapped individuals. To be successful the group will need to be organized sensibly, carefully and professionally; however, this is not beyond the reach of any dedicated person.

The first thing that is needed is a group of people who all share the same aims and who think alike. Once these people have come together, they will need to discuss and research and demand, possible facilities and likely support a new group would receive in the proposed local area. The RDA is of immense value at this stage and will provide literature and the name of the nearest county representative or regional chairman, who will be able to provide advice about the formation of a new group. These people would then be advised to visit an existing group to discover just what is involved and what their expectations might be. Help is also available to new and existing member groups in the form of training videos, top trainers' visits, conferences and member group discussions.

There is much literature and information also available from the RDA:

● *RDA News* – a magazine issued four times a year

● The RDA Handbook (a handbook of general information, including methods, techniques, and procedures)

● List of member groups together with regional and county structure, including regional and county representatives

● Annual reports and accounts

● List of vice-presidents and association officers

● Films produced by the RDA

● Christmas cards

● Driving leaflets

● List of publications

75 *HRH The Princess Royal, GCVO, visiting the Diptford Group, one of the member groups of the RDA of which the Princess Royal is president, where she presented each rider with a commemorative rosette. (RDA)*

Recurring needs

The needs of riders with disabilities are many and varied. They are also on-going. The public can help in many ways to ease the load of responsibility on everyone involved in the Riding for the Disabled movement. Help can be provided in the form of helpers, fundraising, help with secretarial work, or even being willing to help at local functions. Some of the association's many recurring needs are:

Suitable horses and ponies; voluntary helpers; special equipment for riders; training of instructors, therapists and helpers; conference facilities; covered riding schools; sponsorships for publications; films and transportation.

The 1990s

Funds are always needed to finance the needs of riders with disabilities. Without the necessary funds the RDA cannot expand and open the doors of opportunity to severely handicapped people. In the past, member groups have operated mainly in county areas where knowledgeable helpers and suitable ponies are available. In order to give the opportunity to the many handicapped people who live in urban areas purpose-built riding centres are essential.

We also wish to offer more opportunities to adults, many of whom live in these densely populated areas. Many riders with disabilities look forward to riding with us today. We would like so many more to join us tomorrow. (RDA) (75)

10 RIDING IN NORTH AMERICA

North American Riding for the Handicapped Association, Inc. founded in 1969 as a not-for-profit, tax exempt, charitable organization, is today made up of approximately 450 operating centres, and 950 individual members, such as helpers, therapeutic riding instructors, physical and occupational therapists and other members of the medical community, handicapped individuals and their families and friends, researchers, and horse lovers. All are dedicated to the idea that 'the outside of a horse is good for the inside of a person'.

Operating centres range in size from small, one-person programmes serving a handful of individuals to large operations in which several therapeutic riding instructors serve two to three hundred riders each week. Regardless of the size, NARHA's services are available to all:

● a newsletter issued six times each year
● the NARHA guide (a handbook of general information, including methods, techniques, and procedures)
● a NARHA annual directory of operating centres, including state and regional representatives
● voting rights
● discounted prices on workshops and seminars
● discounted prices on various merchandise items

The logo of NARHA (76) appears on all NARHA-associated literature and information

76 *The logo of NARHA*

and is symbolic of the organization's main mission, to promote equine activities for people with disabilities.

NARHA's staff and activities are supported by annual membership dues, individual gifts and donations, corporate and foundation gifts and donations, and grants. NARHA was indeed fortunate in 1989, after great effort on the part of Lida McCowan and her committee, to receive a $1.2 million grant from the Kellogg Foundation (MI). This three-year grant has initiated nine new programmes, including workshops for operating centres, workshops for therapeutic riding instructors, loan programmes for continuing education, loan programmes for special equipment, display and video production, college curriculum materials development, a regional field representatives programme, annual conference support and programme coordination. The implementation of these new programmes will be scattered throughout the term of the grant. Committees and special interest groups are currently working on all aspects of these programmes.

Of the nine new programmes being implemented by the Kellogg Foundation grant, one of the most significant is the workshop education programme. Topics to be covered include the newest information on disabilities treated by therapeutic riding; how to fund a programme; grant writing; publicity and public relations; special equipment – its fitting care, and safety; the role of the physiotherapist in a programme; postural correction – including handling and facilitation tech-

niques; selection of the correct therapy horse for specific disabilities; rider evaluation – initial and on-going; helpers – their selection and training; the latest methods in mounting and dismounting; lesson plans and record keeping; exercises and games; working and schooling the horse on the ground; instructor teaching techniques; and operating centre organization and administration.

The development of various educational curricula in therapeutic riding has also been a major project focus in NARHA. One such project provides a comprehensive programme of riding

77 *Robert D. Douglas, Director, The National Center for Therapeutic Riding, Rock Creek Park, in Washington, DC, and former First Lady Nancy Reagan review riders with mental handicaps at an Equestrian Fest honouring Mrs Reagan's enthusiastic support of riding therapy during her White House years. (Michael Evspell)*

therapy consisting of twenty lessons in each of the following areas: classroom, stable management, and mounted. Each of the twenty lessons is accompanied by adapted occupational and physical therapy exercises. All lessons come with instructional guidelines, teaching materials and classroom handouts. The curriculum is designed to be used by trained, qualified therapeutic riding instructors and is targeted for students five years old and up who have special education needs. Authors of the curriculum are a team of specialists, including a psychologist, an occupational therapist, special educators and riding therapists.[1]

America is a huge country, and the problem of NARHA being an effective organization to meet the variety of needs of its membership, and to cover the vastness of its geographic territory, is an enormous challenge. How has NARHA chosen to deal with this issue? The answer is networking. Networking is a highly organized system to provide a format for improved communication, accessible meetings, and for information-sharing and working together in a close and productive way. One of the most important aspects of networking is the contact of new members and new operating centres to offer assistance and the opportunity for involvement in local, state, regional and national activities; and to assess and meet the specific needs of each region. The NARHA network has proved to be an efficient regional system which provides operating centres and members easy access to current information, educational opportunities, information exchanges and important relationships with others involved in therapeutic riding. It provides a continuous link for communication between the NARHA organization and its members. Important national programmes such as accreditation, instructor certification, NARHA workshops, curriculum projects, the NARHA bibliography, and the annual conference can be introduced at the state and regional meetings. NARHA will soon announce a new programme of regional field representatives. This pro-

gramme will provide twelve national educational consultants whose function will be to visit and assess NARHA operating centres. It might be to help make the application process for accreditation easier, or to give helpful hints on fund raising, or to meet with the programme's board of directors to explain the role of NARHA. The possibilities are unlimited.

NARHA's growth is exciting and with growth often comes change. Change does not mean abandonment of what has been unique about our organization, but it can mean change in ways of doing things. As more people become involved, there is less reason for the organization to depend on any one person. People with fresh ideas bring creativity and newness of thought that is the lifeblood of every healthy organization. To develop thoughtful, flexible, dedicated and creative leadership is the key to NARHA's future. Every member needs to pitch in![2] (77)

About the Delta Society

The Delta Society is a not-for-profit, tax exempt, public service organization dedicated to furthering the beneficial contacts between people and animals. It is a leading international resource on the human–animal bond, whose work covers every aspect of this field, from promoting scientific research examining the nature of human–animal interactions, to helping people start local pet therapy and education programmes, to sponsoring major national and international conferences on the subject.

The Delta Society issues three publications, *Interactions*, a newsletter about current activities in the field, *People–Animals–Environment*, a magazine containing articles about issues and information regarding the human–animal bond, and *Anthrozoos*, a multidisciplinary quarterly journal containing the latest and most significant editorials, scholarly commentary and research on the interactions of people, animals and the environment.

The Delta Society has experienced rapid growth since its inception a little over a decade ago. In 1989 it boasted 2600 individual memberships and 13 affiliated regional chapters, whose member volunteers bring the education and service programmes of the Delta Society to thousands of their local community members. Delta has expanded its resource centre and library, and publishes a resource sheet listing educational materials and videotapes for sale and rent.

The Delta Society has an extensive award programme to honour the people and animals who make significant contributions to the field of human–animal interaction. Among the awards are: therapy horse of the year, the Boris Levinson Memorial Research award, the human–animal bond award, model programme awards, a distinguished service award, the Nabisco grant for a human–animal demonstration project, and the Michael McCulloch memorial award, which was established to provide an annual renewal of the society's mission and commitment to the dream that challenged Dr McCulloch's life and sparked his interest in the establishment of the Delta Society.

Our survival as a species depends on our ability to foster a boundless compassion for living things. A person or a community is not healthy without nurturing contact with animals and nature. (Leo K. Busted, DVM, PhD, President Emeritus, Delta Society)

APPENDIX: TACK AND HORSE TERMS

POINTS OF THE HORSE

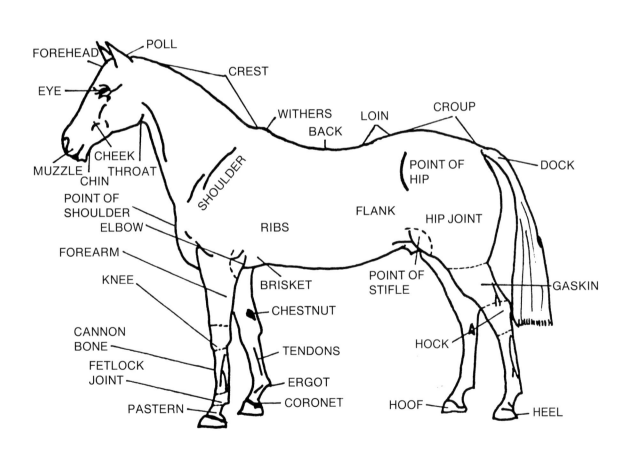

FOREHEAD POLL

CREST

EYE

WITHERS LOIN CROUP

BACK

CHEEK

MUZZLE THROAT

CHIN

POINT OF
HIP

POINT OF
SHOULDER

ELBOW

FOREARM

KNEE

CANNON
BONE

FETLOCK
JOINT

PASTERN

SHOULDER

RIBS

BRISKET

CHESTNUT

TENDONS

ERGOT

CORONET

FLANK

HIP JOINT

POINT OF
STIFLE

HOCK

HOOF

DOCK

GASKIN

HEEL

HORSE'S FOOT

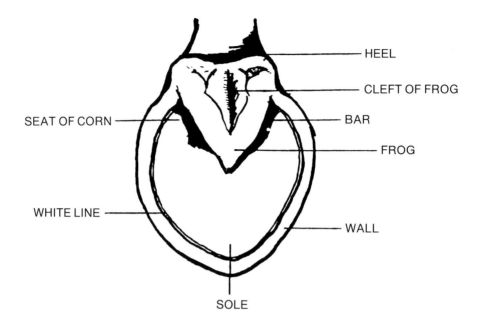

HEEL

CLEFT OF FROG

SEAT OF CORN

BAR

FROG

WHITE LINE

WALL

SOLE

BRIDLE

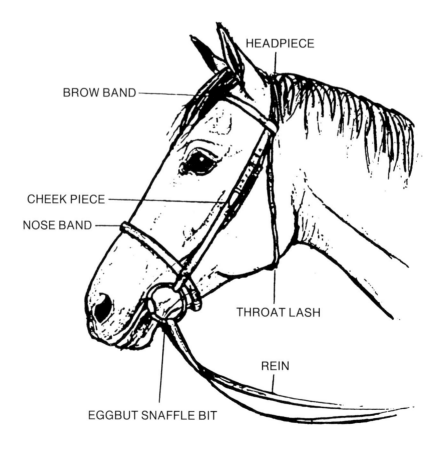

HEADPIECE

BROW BAND

CHEEK PIECE

NOSE BAND

THROAT LASH

REIN

EGGBUT SNAFFLE BIT

HORSES AND PONIES

HEIGHT — are in HANDS (1 hand = 10 cm (4 in)) at the highest point of the WITHERS (*see* Points of the Horse)
AGE — can be estimated by looking at the teeth
COLOUR –

Dark Bay	very dark brown, black mane and tail
Bay	deep brown, black mane and tail
Bright Bay	bright brown, black mane and tail
Black	black all over (white hairs allowed)
Grey	white all over
Dappled Grey	white with dappled spots
Flea-Bitten Grey	white with dark flecks
Iron Grey	dark grey with white hairs in mane and tail
Chestnut	reddish ginger (light or dark) with matching or lighter mane and tail
Liver Chestnut	reddish brown, matching mane and tail
Palomino	gold (light or dark) with cream mane and tail
Piebald	black and white patches
Skewbald	brown and white patches
Red Roan	brown or reddish and white hairs, all over
Blue Roan	black and white hairs all over
Dun	pale beige with black mane and tail

GROOMING EQUIPMENT

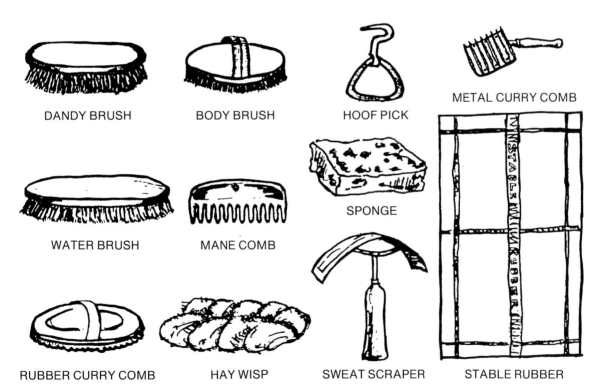

DANDY BRUSH　　BODY BRUSH　　HOOF PICK　　METAL CURRY COMB

WATER BRUSH　　MANE COMB　　SPONGE

RUBBER CURRY COMB　　HAY WISP　　SWEAT SCRAPER　　STABLE RUBBER

GIRTHS AND STIRRUPS

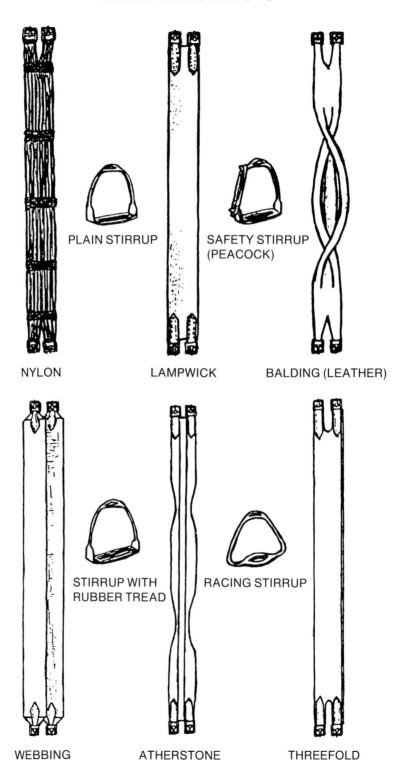

PLAIN STIRRUP

SAFETY STIRRUP
(PEACOCK)

NYLON

LAMPWICK

BALDING (LEATHER)

STIRRUP WITH
RUBBER TREAD

RACING STIRRUP

WEBBING

ATHERSTONE

THREEFOLD

REFERENCES

Introduction

1 The Riding for the Disabled Association (RDA), Avenue R, National Agricultural Centre, Kenilworth, Warwickshire, CV8 2LY.
2 Adapted from the County Report of the United States, selected reading from the Fifth International Congress on Therapeutic Riding, Milan, Italy, 1985. Prepared by Natalie Bieber.
3 Special Olympics International, 1350 New York Avenue, NW, Suite 500, Washington, DC 20005, USA.
4 The Delta Society, 321 Burnett Ave. S, Suite 303, Renton, WA 98055.
5 Penna. Council HRH, Attn.: Ben Nolt, Director, 1 Armsby Building, Penna. State University, University Park, PA 16802.

Chapter 1

1 Heipertz, Wolfgang, *et al.*, (1981). *Therapeutic Riding*, translated by Marion Takeuchi, Ottawa, Ontario, Canada K11 8B9.
2 Developed by Jan Spink, MA, New Harmony Foundation, RR 5, Box 272, Charlottesville, UA 22901, USA.

Chapter 2

1 Engel, Barbara T., M. Galloway, and Bull, Mary P. (1989). *The Horse, The Handicapped, and The Riding Team in a Therapeutic Riding Program, A Training Manual for Volunteers.*
2 Davies, John Anthony. (1988). *The Reins of Life*, J. A. Allen and Co. Ltd., London. p. 17.
3 ACPRD Attn.: Miss G. M. Walker MCSP, Honorary Secretary, The Orchard, Broadlands, Lower Paice Lane, Medstead, Hampshire, GU34 5PX.

Chapter 5

1 Barbara L. Glasow, P.T., Tobyhanna, PA, USA.
2 *An Instructor's View of Hippotherapy*, Jill Palmer, Instructor, Red Barn RDA Group; *A Physiotherapist's View of Hippotherapy*, Frances Thomas-Davies, Wycombe CMHT.

Chapter 6

1 Joswick, Fran, Kitteredge, Marjorie, McCowan, Lida, *et al.* (1986). *Aspects and Answers: A Manual for Therapeutic Horseback Riding Programs*, Cheff Center, Augusta, MI 49012, USA.

Chapter 7

1 and 4 Squadron Leader Don Baker – speaking at the 1989 RDA Driving Conference.

2 RDA Driving Pamphlet, Notes on Administrative Procedures and Safety Code, Section 3.

3 British Driving Society Attn.: Jenny Dillon, Executive Secretary, 27 Dugard Place, Barford, Warwickshire CV35 8DX.

5 NADD, 87 Main Street, Fort Plain, New York 13339, USA.

Chapter 10

1 For further information, contact Marjorie Marani, Kent Association for Riding Therapy, Route 2, Box 235, Chestertown, MD 21620, USA.

2 From a letter from the president, by Judy Lightfoot, *NARHA News*, Vol. 3, No. 1, 1990. p. 2.

USEFUL PUBLICATIONS

Bauer, Joseph. (1976). *Riding for Rehabilitation: A Guide for Handicapped Riders and Their Instructors.* CANRIDE, 209 Deloraine Avenue, Toronto, Canada M5M 2B2.

Burton, Dr. Lee. (1983). *The Value of Riding for the Mentally Handicapped Child.* The Riding for the Disabled Association, Avenue R, National Agricultural Centre, Kenilworth, Warwickshire, CV8 2LY.

Davies, J. A. (revised edition 1988). *The Reins Of Life.* J. A. Allen and Co., 1 Lower Grosvenor Place, Buckingham Palace Road, London, United Kingdom, SW1W 0EL.

Guidelines for Organizing a Horseback Riding Program for Individuals with Disabilities (Bulletin 518A). CSU Bulletin Room, 171 Aylesworth Hall SW, Colorado State University, Fort Collins, CO 80523, USA.

Handbook of the Riding for the Disabled Association (3rd ed). (1984). The Riding for the Disabled Association, Avenue R, National Agricultural Centre, Kenilworth, Warwickshire, United Kingdom, CV8 2LY.

Handbook of the North American Riding for the Handicapped Association. North American Riding for the Handicapped Association, Inc., P.O. Box 33150, Denver, Colorado 80134, USA.

Heipertz, W., Heipertz, C., Kroger, A., and Kuprian, W. (1981). *Therapeutic Riding*, translated by Marion Takeuchi. Canadian Equestrian Federation, 333 River Road, Ottawa, Ontario, Canada K1L 8B9.

Husley, Robin. (1982). *Horseback Riding for the Hearing Impaired: A Practical Guide and Suggested Signs.* Robin Husley, Riding High, Inc., 2392 D Half Moon Drive, St. Louis, MO 63114, USA.

Joswick, F., Kitteredge, M., McCowan, L., *et al.* (1986). *Aspects and Answers: A Manual for Therapeutic Horseback Riding Programs.* Cheff Center for the Handicapped, Box 171, R.R. 1, Augusta, MI 49012, USA.

Lewis, Anne. (1975). *A Guide to Basic Riding Instruction*, J. A. Allen and Co., London.

Littauer, Vladimir S. (1974). *Commonsense Horsemanship* (the section on how to teach riding, pp. 321–65), ARCO Publishing Co., New York, USA.

Longden, Mary L. (1984). *Teaching Disabled Riders.* Acacia Press PTY Ltd, P.O. Box 22, Blackburn 3030, Victoria, Australia.

McCowan, Lida L. (1978). *It Is Ability That Counts*. Cheff Center for the Handicapped, Box 171, R.R. 1, Augusta, MI 49012, USA.

Morris, George H. (1981). *George Morris Teaches Beginners to Ride*, Doubleday and Co., Garden City, NY, USA.

Mortimer, Monty (1983). *The Riding Instructor's Handbook*, David and Charles, Newton Abbot, Devon.

Podhajsky, Alois (1973). *The Riding Teacher*, Doubleday and Co., Garden City, NY, USA.

Proceedings of the Fourth International Congress on Therapeutic Riding. (1982). Kuratorium fur Therapeutisches Reiten, e.V., Frieherr-von-Langen Strasse 13, 4410 Warendorf, West Germany. (Publication in German.)

Proceedings of the Fifth International Congress on Therapeutic Riding. (1985). Therapeutic Riding Services, P.O. Box 41, Riderwood, MD 21139, USA. (Publication in English.)

Riede, D. (1986). *Aspects of Therapeutic Riding*, translated by J. F. Allen, edited by J. M. Tebay. Therapeutic Riding Services, P.O. Box 41, Riderwood, MD 21139, USA. (Publication in English.)

Riede, D. (1988). *Physiotherapy on the Horse*, translated by Angela Dusenbury, PT, edited by J. M. Tebay. Omnipress, Inc., The Delta Society, 321 Burnett Avenue South, Suite 303, Renton, WA 98055, USA. (Publication in English.)

Roberts, Pamela (1987). *Teaching the Child Rider*, J. A. Allen and Co., 1 Lower Grosvenor Place, Buckingham Palace Road, London SW1W 0EL.

Soloman, Diane S. (1982). *Teaching Riding*, University of Oklahoma Press, Norman, OK, USA.

Stanier, Sylvia. *The Art of Lungeing*, J. A. Allen and Co., 1 Lower Grosvenor Place, Buckingham Palace Road, London SW1W 0EL.

The Instructor's Handbook, (1989). The British Horse Society, Threshold Books Ltd., 661 Fulham Rd., London.

Wright, Gordon and Kelley, Michael. (1975). *The Riding Instructor's Manual*, Doubleday and Co., Garden City, NY, USA.

The RDA Official Manual, (1990). The Riding for the Disabled Association, The Kenilworth Press Limited, 661 Fulham Road, London SW6 5PZ.

USEFUL ADDRESSES

Association of Chartered Physiotherapists in Riding for the Disabled
Hon. Secretary: Geraldine Walker
The Orchard
Broadlands
Lower Paice Lane
Medstead
Hants GU34 5PX
Great Britain

The British Driving Society
27 Dugard Place
Barford
Warwick CV35 8DX
Great Britain

The British Horse Society
British Equestrian Centre
Stoneleigh
Kenilworth
Warwickshire CV8 2LR
Great Britain

The Cheff Center
RR 1 Box 171
Augusta MI 49012
USA

The Chartered Society of Physiotherapy
14 Bedford Row
London WC1R 4ED
Great Britain

The Delta Society
Century Buildings
Suite 303
321 Burnett Avenue South
Renton Washington 98055
USA

The Fortune Centre of Riding Therapy
Avon Tyrell
Bransgore
Nr Christchurch
Dorset BH23 8EE
Great Britain

North American Riding for the Handicapped Assc
PO Box 33150
Denver Colorado 80134
USA

PA Council – Horseback Riding for the Handicapped
Pennsylvania Council/HRH
1 Armsby Building
Pennsylvania State University, University Park
Pennsylvania 16802
USA

The Pony Club
(as BHS)

Riding for the Disabled Association
Avenue "R"
National Agricultural Centre
Kenilworth
Warwickshire CV8 2LY
Great Britain

RDA International
Secretary: Miss Jane Wykeham-Musgrave
Poultmoor Farm
Barnsley
Cirencester
Glos GL7 5EQ
Great Britain

INDEX